The People Problem

The People

Dean Fraser

Problem

What You Should Know

about Growing Population

and Vanishing Resources

INDIANA UNIVERSITY PRESS

Bloomington / London

301.3
F 841 p

14 8004

SECOND PRINTING 1972

Copyright © 1971 by Indiana University Press
All rights reserved

No part of this book may be reproduced or utilized in any form
or by any means, electronic or mechanical, including photocopying
and recording, or by any information storage and retrieval system,
without permission in writing from the publisher. The Association
of American University Presses Resolution on Permissions constitutes
the only exception to this prohibition.

Published in Canada by Fitzhenry & Whiteside Limited,
Don Mills, Ontario
Library of Congress catalog card number: 77-143245
ISBN: 253-16175-4
Manufactured in the United States of America

MOUNT UNION COLLEGE
LIBRARY

Contents

Part I / The Nature of Biological Populations

1. Exponential Expansion • 3

Introduction   3
The Newspaper Game   6
The Coin Game   8
Bacterial Growth   9
The Human Population   13
Instant Immortality   15
Maximum Populations   22
Fluctuating Populations and Regulation   23
Extinction   26
Summary   27

Part II / Factors Limiting Population Growth

2. Space • 31

Housing vs. Food   32
Water vs. Food   32
Recreation Space   33
Conservation   34
Transportation   35
Space Projections   36
The Wild Blue Yonder   38
Summary   39

Contents

3. *Food* · *40*

Agricultural Opulence   *41*
Current Malnutrition   *42*
Food Surpluses and Distribution   *44*
Food for the Future   *46*
Food from the Sea   *52*
Agricultural Efficiency   *57*
New Foods   *65*
The End of the Miracle   *71*
Summary   *75*

4. *Water* · *78*

Water Recycling   *80*
Human Water Needs   *81*
Water Resources   *88*
Improving the Efficiency of Water Use   *94*
Summary   *103*

5. *Mineral Resources and Energy* · *104*

Copper   *104*
Other Metals   *106*
Non-metals   *108*
Energy Requirements   *108*
Fossil Fuels   *113*
Nuclear Energy   *114*
Summary   *117*

6. *Pollution* · *119*

Introduction   *119*
Air Pollution   *121*
Water Pollution   *135*

CONTENTS

ULTIMATE DISPOSAL   *155*
SOLID WASTES   *168*
NOISE POLLUTION   *174*
THE PROSPECTS   *176*

7. *Competitors* • *180*

Et Tu Brute?   *184*
SUMMARY   *187*

PART III / POPULATION CONTROL

8. *Birth, Population, and Death* • *191*

POPULATION CONTROL—WHO WANTS HOW MUCH?   *194*
WHO DOESN'T WANT BIRTH CONTROL?   *196*
METHODS OF BIRTH CONTROL   *214*
NATIONAL PROGRAMS   *221*
THE TRAP   *229*
SUMMARY   *231*

Epilogue   *233*

Suggested Readings   *241*

Index   *243*

Figures

Fig. 1   The Exponential Growth of Bacteria   *10*

Fig. 2   Human Population Growth Compared with
          Bacterial Growth   *12*

Fig. 3   Doubling Time of the Human Population   *16*

Fig. 4   Human Death Rates   *17*

Fig. 5   Measured Water Usage in the United States   *87*

Fig. 6   Energy Sources in the United States   *110*

Fig. 7   Electrical Power Consumption in the
          United States   *112*

Fig. 8   Decline of Desirable Fish in Lake Erie   *143*

Fig. 9   Aging Indicators   *144*

Part I

The Nature

of Biological

Populations

1 /

Exponential Expansion

Population, when unchecked, increases in a geometric ratio.

—MALTHUS

INTRODUCTION

A PRINCIPAL OBJECT OF THIS BOOK is to teach you to multiply by two. Not *how* to multiply by two, simply to do it, to think of the human population problem not as something that sneaked up on us in some inexplicable way, but rather in terms of simple biological and mathematical laws—the accrual of finally staggering numbers by the elementary process of continuous doubling.

The present and future complications caused by human population are really not at all mysterious nor unexpected. We keep hearing about the "population problem," as if it were occasioned by some quite unexplained and sudden "explosion" of human numbers, as an inevitable "potential disaster." Writers who should know better cast about for a culprit, and we mutter darkly about the intransigence of the Catholic church or the unbridled reproduction of the Chinese and Indians. It is time, however, that we understood that nothing arcane or sinister is involved; that the immediate villain, if any, is progress in solving human health problems. Improvement in average life expectancy almost world-wide has indeed sharply (if somewhat temporarily) increased the ap-

3

parent doubling rate of the human species, but even without twentieth-century medicine we would still very soon have been in serious population difficulties. The fact, as we shall see, is that the human race has expanded to a point of near saturation of its habitat (the earth). When this happens to any biological species, trouble, caused by quite simple and natural processes, is around a very nearby corner if the population of that species continues to increase exponentially. Unfortunately, this fact is little understood; the accretion of population by a regular doubling—that is, exponential expansion—is quite outside of our normal experience. A main purpose of this book is to provide the necessary experience.

But even though the human population problem is a natural one, it cannot be ignored. Because it is THE PROBLEM. Everything that we know about biological populations tells us that the human race cannot and will not increase indefinitely. If we knew nothing about biology, common sense would lead to the same conclusion. At the present growth rate the human race will beyond argument be facing its most important crisis probably within the lifetimes of our children. I hope that I can convince you of this even though no one can say definitely when the crisis will occur, far less what its consequences will be.

But if this is true, why are we by and large complacent, for it is the complacency that is to me the most worrisome factor. We clearly have the capacity to solve the problem; why are we largely ignoring it except for a little circumspect nibbling at the edges of such population-caused difficulties as pollution and food supply? I think that at least a part of the answer is that we live lives surrounded by "disaster," "catastrophe," "unimaginable human tragedy." The communications media pile upon us every day superlatives of all kinds—a smallpox epidemic in Nepal is known to every person in the United States within hours, as is an earthquake in Terra del Fuego, or a juicy axe murder in Barking Creek. Ours is a period when crisis and the unimaginable have become not only commonplace but demanded. One can no longer sell newspapers with announcements of meetings of the Ladies' Missionary Society. Most of the incredible creations of the Jules Vernes, H. G. Wellses, Aldous Huxleys of a prior generation have become old stuff, long ago surpassed by the publicity releases from NASA. Many of the wildest imaginings of the creators of pulp thrillers have either come to pass or seem readily credible and within our grasp. If, tomorrow, flying saucers turn out indeed to be real and peopled by a race of superior beings bent on our enslavement as bonbons for their offspring, the average citizen would as likely as not hear this over television as an interruption of a Late Show horror movie. He would no doubt comment that he expected all along that there was something phony about them damned saucers, that Washington should have done something about them years ago instead of sweeping them under the rug, and that the Defense Department better come up with something pretty good after all the money they spent. During the commercial he will go hurriedly to the john and then get another cold beer so that he can settle back comfortably to be apprised of the latest developments and told how omnipotent science is coping with them.

Death rays, space stations, colonies on Mars, wholesale death from biological warfare or nerve gas, devastation by nuclear bombs, eradication of humans by the tens of millions within an hour or so: all well within one's grasp, been expecting them for years. The population problem? Another "catastrophe"? Really old hat. Malthus, the celebrated English economist, predicted incipient disaster over 150 years ago. His predictions were so wrong and have so often been held up to ridicule as examples of the futility of further warnings that the very words "Malthusian philosophy" are not infrequently used pejoratively by the complacent or those with axes to grind to dismiss any and all discussion of future population problems. Largely neglected, however, is the fact that Malthus' basic theory could not have been more correct. His spe-

5

cific predictions of the exhaustion of resources were based on faulty facts, and therein lies the ground for dismissal of his conclusions. Today, of course, we have available far more complete data on which to base projections. Even though there is no single area in which one can make concrete prediction of inescapable disaster from extrapolation of present trends, there are plenty in which experts foresee serious difficulties, beginning right now and becoming exacerbated in the near future. Another object of this book, then, is to gather together some of the more compelling of these facts and try to point to probable future developments. None of these facts is new, most have appeared in current popular or semipopular periodicals or books. But what is impressive is the totality of them and the sense of urgency that such a compilation suggests. In some five or six years of accumulation of the available data, I find that I have vacillated between agreeing with those who dismiss present alarm as neo-Malthusian lack of faith in the future or with the group that thinks we may already be too late to avoid a singularly unpleasant, all too imminent doom of the human. In describing the facts as I see them, I shall try to present both sides.

Malthus pointed out that the numbers of humans tended to increase exponentially whereas resources and production were limited. By exponential expansion we mean in this instance, that the population tends to double at a constant rate. The idea is so basic to an understanding of our present and future difficulties that it deserves illustration.

THE NEWSPAPER GAME

AN OLD PARLOR RIDDLE involves the question of how many times one would have to fold a Sunday newspaper to reach the sun (some 93 million miles away). Beginning with a one inch thick sheaf, on folding it the stack is doubled to two inches; another fold gives four inches, a third fold eight, etc. It is obvious to anyone that a doubling process mounts up, yet in posing this question I find that people often guess one would have to fold the paper a million times. The correct answer is about forty-three times, and since this almost always seems completely incredible—as, of course, it was intended to seem—and since this very simple calculation lies at the heart of my whole thesis, I have given the numbers in Table 1. Please note that nothing is involved beyond the simple ability to multiply each number in

TABLE 1

FOLDING A ONE INCH THICK NEWSPAPER TO FORM A STACK
THAT WILL REACH THE SUN

Fold	*Thickness*	*Fold*	*Thickness*
1	2″	23	64 miles
2	4″	24	128 miles
3	8″	25	256 miles
4	16″ or over 1 foot	26	512 miles
5	2′	27	over 1,000 miles
6	4′	28	2,000 miles
7	8′	29	4,000 miles
8	16′	30	8,000 miles
9	32′	31	16,000 miles
10	64′	32	32,000 miles
11	128′	33	64,000 miles
12	256′	34	128,000 miles
13	512′	35	256,000 miles
14	1,028′	36	512,000 miles
15	2,056′	37	over 1 million miles
16	4,112′	38	2 million miles
17	8,224′ or over 1 mile	39	4 million miles
18	2 miles	40	8 million miles
19	4 miles	41	16 million miles
20	8 miles	42	32 million miles
21	16 miles	43	64 million miles
22	32 miles	44	over 100 million miles

turn by *two* and to round the results off to feet and miles—a task that can be easily performed by any fourth grader.*

THE COIN GAME

A VERY SIMILAR PROBLEM I learned early from my father. He asked whether I would rather be paid a million dollars a day or receive a penny the first day, then double the amount each succeeding day. Any innocent small boy will take the million dollars a day, and I suspect he is right, because obviously the other scheme is not going to continue for very long once the proponent realizes what confronts him. Basically the problem is identical to the newspaper one, of course, and on his twenty-eighth day the exponential wage-earner would pass his more conservative colleague. On his forty-fourth day he would receive all of the money in stock in the United States and by the fiftieth day he would own the entire wealth of the world.

A peculiar characteristic of both of these numbers problems is that for a long time nothing much seems to happen, then suddenly the numbers jump astronomically. At the end of his second five-day work week, for example, the exponentially paid boy would have received only $5.12 for the day. The newspaper, also, was only thirty-two miles thick when we had used

---

*For those who wish to check this or any similar calculation, the problem is, of course, more simply done by the use of logarithms. The series involves powers, of the number *two*. Thus the number wanted can be stated mathematically as 2^n.

Here $1 \text{ inch} \times 2^n = 93 \times 10^6 \text{ miles} \times 5.3 \times 10^3 \text{ feet/mile} \times 12 \text{ inches/foot}$
$$2^n = 5.9 \times 10^{12}$$
Hence $n \log 2 = \log (5.9 \times 10^{12}) = 12.77$
$$n = \frac{12.77}{0.301} = 42.4$$

The requisite number of folds of a one inch newspaper, then, is between forty-two and forty-three exactly as calculated by simple arithmetic.

up half of our forty-three folds. Just before the last fold, it was only half-way to the sun. We shall return very shortly to this peculiar characteristic of exponential expansions.

Presented with the answers and even demonstration of how the numbers increase, it is still tempting to think that there is some trickery in the arithmetic or that the sort of numerical progression I have described has no relevance to real situations. One *cannot* fold a newspaper, nor any paper, more than a very few—perhaps about eight—times. No one was ever paid by the sort of peculiar scheme I have suggested. It is tempting to say flatly that all of this is simply playing with numbers. Nothing could be farther from the truth.

BACTERIAL GROWTH

THE REPRODUCTION of many one-celled organisms occurs exactly by a process of doubling. One cell enlarges, then divides yielding two. In another generation one has four, then eight, sixteen, etc. In working with bacteria, it all too often becomes apparent that once the population becomes visible to the naked eye things go fast indeed. In fact, with an ordinary test tube containing perhaps a couple of tablespoons of broth as a nutrient, it is possible to begin with a single bacterial cell one afternoon and to have in this small tube by the next morning more bacteria than there are people alive today. This is on the assumption that the bacteria divide once every twenty to thirty minutes, a reasonable average time for many bacteria under ordinary laboratory conditions. The numbers involved (shown in Fig. 1) are, of course, fundamentally those we have seen already in the newspaper and coin problems, but in this instance they represent perfectly real, living organisms, inexorably increasing by steady doubling.

If the process were to continue indefinitely at the rate we have described, say one doubling every half-hour, it is quite easy

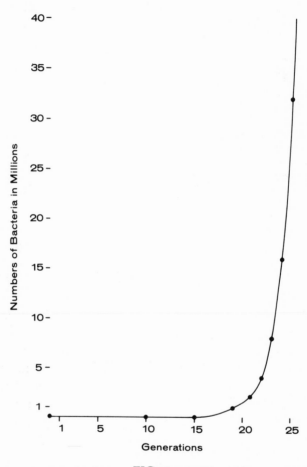

FIG. 1
THE EXPONENTIAL GROWTH OF BACTERIA

to calculate, just by continuing your multiplying by two, that small though the individual cell may be (about a cubic micron or 0.000,000,000,000,06 cubic inches), they would form a solid packed cube of bacteria one mile on each side in some ninety-two divisions, which would require forty-six hours. Continuing this calculation it can be seen that at the 118th division (only fifty-nine hours) they would cover the earth one mile deep. By 173 divisions the orbit of the earth would be packed and the entire solar system would be solid bacteria in less than four days. Perhaps this is the cheapest way to achieve interplanetary travel—on a wave of ebulliently growing bacteria. There would be those, of course, who would object to the smell.

Now manifestly this is not going to happen, science fiction to the contrary notwithstanding. The reasons why it will not happen are pretty obvious, and they are basic to our whole argument. The bacteria in the laboratory are growing in a glass tube of some fixed size. They are contained within this space. But long before they could grow out of the tube in search of new worlds to conquer, they would confront insurmountable problems. Usually the first difficulty is that they run out of some essential nutrient. Another possibility is that when the population achieves its maximum density, the cells are consuming food, or perhaps air, faster than it can be fed to them under their crowded conditions. The culture medium may accumulate metabolic products—waste products—of the cells to the point where they are poisoned. The water available will no longer wash the wastes away nor dilute them adequately. In a natural, nonlaboratory growing condition, the bacteria will sooner or later run into competitors. Viruses may attack them fatally, paramecia may devour them, other organisms may take their food supply from them or poison them.

The net result, of course, is that the bacteria do *not* grow indefinitely but, as suggested in Fig. 2, taper off into a state of constant population density and then, eventually, begin to die. Oddly enough the interrelationships of conditions that actually control these latter stages are not exactly defined even in the simple instance of bacterial growth. But it is clear that such factors as those just cited can and do control ultimate population size.

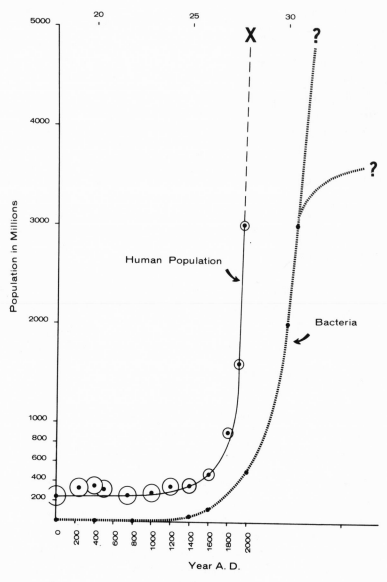

FIG. 2
POPULATION GROWTH

1. / Exponential Expansion

THE HUMAN POPULATION

THE SKEPTIC WILL POINT OUT that humans are not bacteria nor do they multiply by dividing. But the principles that apply to the general problem of population growth are the same. Given the estimates of demographers of the size of the human population at various times in history, we can *calculate* an average doubling time by simple arithmetic, or, more accurately, by somewhat more complicated mathematics. We have mentioned in a previous footnote the use of logarithms for such calculations. But a more accurate way of calulating the rate of growth of the human population is to consider that the numbers increase in the same way as a sum of money at a given rate of interest continuously compounded.* The estimates of population indicated in Table 2 and plotted in Fig. 2 are generally accepted with the understanding that the more recent data are accurate and the earliest ones little more than the best expert guess, but not seriously in error for purposes of the present discussion. By simply glancing at the figures one can estimate an average doubling time for any particular period. But it is then obvious that the human in one sense is alarmingly different from the

---

*Formulas and tables for these numbers are available from a variety of sources such as scientific handbooks, bank interest tables, books on statistics. A reasonably good and simpler approximation is provided by the relation:

$$A = P (1 + i)^n$$

where A is the amount after n years from an initial amount P invested at a rate of interest i, compounded annually. Thus, since the present rate of increase of the human population is 2 percent per year, the population, A, for any future year, n years from now, can be obtained from the present world population of 3.5 billion by the formula:

$$A = 3.5 \times 10^9 \times (1.02)^n$$

The compound interest formula can also be used to calculate the average rate of increase (i) per year between any two dates at which the population is known.

TABLE 2

POPULATION OF THE WORLD*

Year (A.D.)	Approximate Population in Millions
0	200–300
250	325
500	325
1000	275
1200	350
1400	375
1500	450
1600	500
1700	700
1800	900
1900	1,600
1960	3,000

During the early centuries of the Christian era, recurrent epidemics and warfare kept the population from strong growth. Since 1000 A.D. growth has been steady except for the considerable decline caused by the great plague of 1348 in Europe.

bacteria. Whereas we ascribed to them a constant doubling time of about a half-hour, *the human doubling time has continually decreased*, and now stands at about thirty-five years, corresponding to a rate of increase of human population of two percent per year. In other words we have not been content to expand our numbers exponentially at a constant rate but have compounded the crime by multiplying ever faster. What is worse, the figures given are world-wide averages, and in several areas of the world the doubling time is about twenty-five. years and edging downward.

*These figures have been synthesized from "How Many People Have Ever Lived on Earth" by Annabelle Desmond, published in *The Population Crisis and the Use of World Resources* edited by Stuart Mudd and others, Bloomington: Indiana University Press, 1964.

1. / *Exponential Expansion*

INSTANT IMMORTALITY

IF YOU ARE ADDICTED TO SENSATIONAL PROJECTIONS, you can entertain yourself by extrapolating the doubling time. The big boff comes when you reach the conclusion (Fig. 3) that by the year 2040 it will be zero—that is to say people at birth will bear children immediately after zero gestation, far less the other formalities that ordinarily precede the event. I have included this example mainly to illustrate the well-known dangers of extrapolation—the prediction of future events or facts apparently on the basis of those presently known. Let me say, however, that a not too dissimilar conclusion was presented, if much more elaborately and quite soberly, a few years ago in *Science* magazine, a most respectable publication of the American Association for the Advancement of Science. Everyone will perhaps rest easier by knowing that this particular catastrophe is singularly unlikely. As Ansley Coale, a well-known demographer, pointed out in one of many indignant replies to the article in *Science*, we may assume that the human will not be perverse enough to try to avoid the usual nine months' gestation, nor the ordinary age limits of childbearing—say from age fifteen to fifty for the average woman. One then arrives at a finite doubling time of twelve years (a 6 percent rate of increase) even if one assumes that by that time humans will live forever.

Living forever, while we are on the subject, is a concept that the young regard as attractive and that can be made to seem feasible by another seemingly plausible extrapolation of what look like good facts. From Fig. 4 it seems hard to escape the conclusion that in about A.D. 2020 the death rate will have dropped to zero. Seemingly if you can stagger on until then, you got it made—you'll live forever.

But even leaving out of consideration the salutary population-moderating influences of the automobile and cigarette, this is a

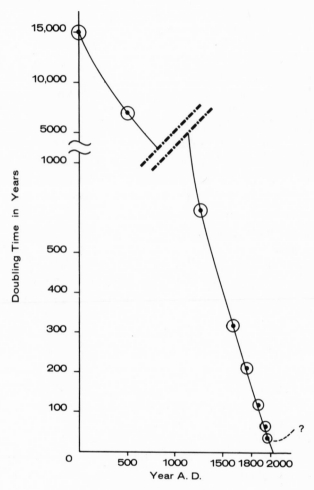

FIG. 3
Doubling Time of the Human Race

possibility that can scarcely be taken seriously. The apparent trend toward infinitely long life represents *average length of life* or *expectancy at birth* and comes very largely from greatly de-

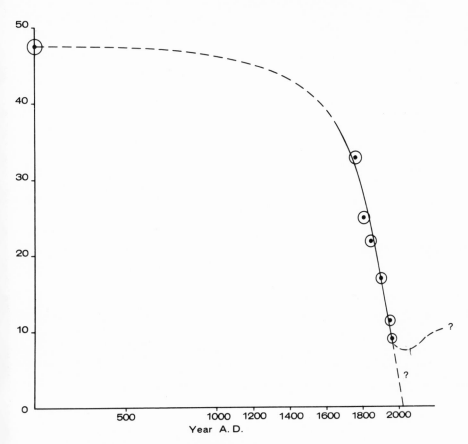

FIG. 4
HUMAN DEATH RATES

creased infant mortality all over the world, not from a significant increase in the *life spans* of those dying from old age. Since
one of the most important causes of the present population crisis
is increased *average length of life*, we should pay a little attention
to what may seem at first a slightly confusing matter—the difference between *average length of life, life expectancy,* and *life
span. Average length of life* is exactly what it says. One adds the

numbers of years that each individual in a group lived and divides by the number in the group. *Life expectancy* is a hypothetical number. Based essentially on death rates, it is the number of years that an individual of a given age may *expect* to live on the average, assuming a complex interplay of factors thought to influence members of his group. *Life span* is the maximum age that any member of the group may attain, in other words, maximum longevity. In a stable situation, life expectancy at birth and average life length should be equal. At such a time as the present (especially in many developing countries), when health conditions are improving rapidly, expectation at birth may greatly exceed the observed actual current average length of life, which tells only what *has* happened while expectancy is a projection into the future. Consider a pioneer family in the United States that had ten children. Let us make the assumption that four died at birth, one at two years, two at three years, one at five, one at eight, and one at a ripe ninety-seven years. The average life length of children in the family, then, was 11.8 years. In a parallel (if unlikely) United States family of ten today, we might assume that one infant dies and the rest live to their late sixties or early seventies, leading to an average life of, perhaps, some sixty-three years without a single person having lived within twenty-five years as long as the nonagenarian of the pioneer group.

A considerable difficulty with the present statistics is that a sharp decrease in infant mortality has left us, at the moment, with a large proportion of the world population in the fecund prime of life with a very low death rate. When we come to equilibrium with respect to age distribution, the rate will level off.

What that rate will be can be argued from a number of bases, but we can make an approximation from the following considerations:

It is generally agreed that one may discount the biblical stories of Methuselah on the basis that something may have been lost in translation. The issue should also not be confused by such common instances as the ancient gentleman in my natal town who was amiably conceded to have celebrated a birthday at least each six months in his last decade. Authenticated records of modern times (post-1700) indicate that the greatest age attained was 113 years 124 days. This then would be the accepted *human life span*. It seems clear that the human dying of "old age" today is little older than similar people in earliest historical times. One can argue that there is no evolutionary advantage to life span beyond the age insuring the successful passing on of a particular set of genes. Certainly there is none in prolonging life beyond breeding and child-supporting age. In fact there is every argument for believing that we are genetically programmed to die in the interests of genetic and social progress. Eschewing as a youthful excess the present view of our children that age thirty is a logical time for euthanasia, nature *will* take care of us. There seems no predictable likelihood that medical achievements now in view will extend the aged human to a life span of much more than 100 years.

Presumably the death rate will not drop to zero in A.D. 2020 but will level off at something like ten per 1000 people per year.*

But there is a peculiar phenomenon observable at present and leading temporarily to an artificially low death rate. To understand the situation, let us simplify it and assume both that the average life length is thirty-three years and that every person lives exactly to age thirty-three and then dies, leading to a death rate of 1/33 per person per year or thirty per 1000 people per year—a situation actually obtaining in Mexico as recently as 1930.

---

*The human population is divided not only into male and female, but into those who, like me, adore numbers and the comforting noise they make when sloshing about in one's mind vs. those who, like my wife, cannot abide figures. For the benefit of the former I have included in several places in this book various numerical discussions. But for the relief of the latter I am separating such nauseous material into tables and figures. The idea is that the text will make sense, hopefully, even if this sort of material is totally skipped.

Now assume a miraculous medical discovery that extends the average life to age 100, with, again, the simplifying if nonsensical assumption that every person lives to age 100 and then dies. Obviously for sixty-seven years no one dies; *the death rate has dropped to zero.* Eventually, of course, it will return to the rate characteristic of an average life length of 100 years of ten per 1000 per year. The point is that we are now very much in that position world-wide. Through control of insects and disease, the life expectancy in Mexico—to pursue this example—has indeed suddenly increased from thirty-two years in 1930 to forty-eight years in 1950 to about sixty-three years currently. In the United States and other highly developed countries we have become very expert at keeping people alive to the point where they die of "old age." The result is that the present death rate of about 9.4 per 1000 per year is actually lower than the rate of ten per 1000 to be expected if we lived to an average age of 100 instead of the current expectancy of seventy years.

If, however, we accept the current opinion of a number of medical authorities that with all the craft at their disposal for the foreseeable future, people will still wear out because of seemingly inherent genetic limitations at about age 100, we are left with an eventual levelled-out rate of some ten per 1000.

We now need to consider the birth rate which varies widely, depending very largely on the degree of development of the area under consideration. In highly developed areas we see figures such as the nineteen per 1000 per year figure of Europe as a whole or twenty for the U.S.S.R. According to widely accepted opinion, these figures represent the social consequences of urbanization and industrialization. They are also doubtless aided by a much diminished influence of the Catholic church. At the other extreme we have forty-five for southern Asia, forty-two for Latin America, and forty-nine for Africa.

The present world average level of thirty-three births per 1000 people per year is somewhat heightened by the youthful average age of the world population, but as an approximation to the net rate of gain in human population we can subtract a projected death rate of ten from this figure to see a gain of twenty-three people per 1000 per year. On this assumption then—that we continue to improve medical postponement of death to the probable genetic limitation of age 100 and continue the present birth rate—we are left with a catastrophic doubling time for the human race of about thirty-one years (2¼ percent rate of increase). This is a rate of growth slightly greater than the current figure of thirty-five years used for the various projections made in this book.

To slow population growth, we must do one of two things. We must allow the death rate to increase (a suggestion that gets made sooner or later in nearly every discussion of the population problem) or we must lower the birth rate. It is generally accepted that the human birth rate has, with minor fluctuations, been reasonably constant over the world for a long time—probably at least for all of recorded history. This is presumably a tribute to the constancy of the libido and the inefficiency of methods of birth control for all time up to the present century. But we now have operating a number of factors that tend to lower the birth rate. Classically urbanization and industrialization have impelled couples toward the desire for smaller families. With modern birth control and education this desire can be expressed in accomplishment. A dramatic example is Japan, where the maximum birth rate of thirty-six per 1000 per year in 1920 has dropped to a current rate of fourteen leading to a doubling time of 143 years. If this figure could be achieved world-wide I think that even the doom sayers among us could face the future with some equanimity.

The world, of course, *is* urbanizing, faster than the people can be accommodated in most places. It *is* industrializing. In many areas family planning *is* being tolerated if not pushed. The question is how far natural forces and haphazard application of birth control will go toward solving our problems. How soon can we anticipate a levelling off of the rate of growth? At what numbers of humans? Will catastrophe be the only force great enough to secure a tolerable population? Do we face a "brave new world" in which the number of children per family will be legislated? What kind of standard of living will we have when a stationary population has been reached? How much time do we have to solve these problems? What are the limiting factors?

These problems and the facts bearing on them are the subject of the remaining sections of this book. For the fact is that the human population *must* eventually achieve a maximum number. We believe this to be so from common sense and for a number of reasons that will be presented in subsequent chapters concerned with obvious limiting factors. We also know very well that all biological populations from bacteria to whales may increase at phenomenal rates under certain conditions but eventually achieve a state of zero growth. The important question is how soon this can or will occur with humans, since the consequences will be quite different if we stabilize in ten rather than in 100 years.

Although our main interest lies in consideration of pressures that may act on the human race to determine the feasible eventual level, it is apropos to consider what we know about populations of other living things. There is considerable literature on this subject and a great deal of current interest.

MAXIMUM POPULATIONS

INHERENT IN THE ABOVE *reductio ad absurdum* of the example of unlimited bacterial growth is the manifest certainty that for any species there must be some limiting number. What happens when that number is reached? One might assume that the species would then remain stationary in numbers, with a steady birth rate, death rate, food supply, allocation of space, etc. But how long a time period would constitute proof of such a stable relationship with the environment? And how large an area must one consider—a single test tube of bacteria, a field of mice, the entire world population of dinosaurs? We know that some species have existed for very long periods of time (in the tens of millions of years), but the very nature of evolution suggests that most populations eventually succumb to changes in their surroundings. Thus the "stable population" is at best a sometime thing —though I suspect that we would be very happy in a few decades if we could achieve even a fairly short term stability for the human population. But of this more anon.

FLUCTUATING POPULATIONS AND REGULATION

THE ATTENTION OF ECOLOGISTS has been focused in recent years on a fascinating problem—that of populations of animals that fluctuate, sometimes within very wide limits over fairly predictable periods. Though this problem is of obvious importance to our understanding of the behavior of populations, we shall not devote much time to the really intriguing observations. One reason is the question of the relevancy of this strange, if widespread, type of behavior to the human situation. There may be important lessons to be learned; there may not. But there is a second, fairly annoying reason. Even very careful and intensive study has not revealed the basic cause of the phenomenon. On the contrary, all of the obvious and pat assumptions that had been made at the outset were wrong or at least not crucial.

A classical and widely known example is that of the lemming. It has been observed for centuries that these small mammals periodically appear in incredibly huge numbers seemingly out of nowhere and then disappear as suddenly and mysteriously. The widely believed story of the entire race suddenly swimming out to sea to drown by the millions in some romantically futile grand gesture of mass hara-kiri seems, like many enchanting zoological folk tales, to be pretty much mythical. But it is true that the population does go through startling fluctuations. Study has shown that this example, while particularly dramatic, is far from unique. In fact it may be that such cyclic behavior of the population of any given area with respect to any given creature may be very common if not the rule. Field mice, ticks, rabbits and a number of other animals behave similarly. In explanation, one might assume that the species ate up all of the food and died, or that they became so crowded that an epidemic or mouse-Armageddon wiped them nearly out. Or they might have contaminated their surroundings or attracted an overbalance of predators by their very numbers. Suffice it to say that all of these obvious ideas and a considerable number of more ingenious and sophisticated notions have been tested and discarded as the major cause even though all of them are at times involved to one degree or another.

Although we do not really understand population regulation, there is one observation that has proved particularly intriguing because of its obvious implications with respect to humans. Several species, notably rats, under crowded natural or laboratory conditions, tend to reduce their birth rate sharply as though in some built-in effort to compensate for the crowding. Those among us who would like to believe that this is the best of all possible worlds and that Divine Providence is the solution to everything, seize eagerly on this observation as evidence that a similar process will save the human race. Careful sociological observation, however, has not supported the idea that the most undesirable of crowded ghetto conditions establishes a reduced human birth rate. On the contrary. We seem to lack the sound instincts (to use a word that explains nothing) of rats.

If we are to derive a take-home lesson from these studies, it is that for every species considered there has always been a maximum level of numbers able to survive under particular conditions. This level was *not* usually achieved along with comfy coexistence. On the contrary, in natural populations quite regularly an apparent overshooting of stability occurs, resulting in population decline nearly to the vanishing point followed by the beginning of a new cycle. Regulation exists, indeed, but at the expense of seemingly disastrous alternations of feast and famine. It would be more pleasant if we did not see the possibility that the human race has reached a point of crowding that may very easily lead to famine—as we shall see—or possibly to ruinous nuclear warfare between the haves and have-nots, or to mass death from epidemic and/or overpollution.

At any rate, although we have no reason to predict that the human race is subject to far-reaching fluctuations on a worldwide level, we should at least note that the *rise* of such populations is indeed parallel to the present human situation and for the same reason. The awe-inspiring torrents of certain species that have been noted throughout history are simply examples of exponential expansion in a favorable environment; the dramatically sudden appearance of large populations is not at all inexplicable when one understands the nature of exponential processes, as indicated in Fig. 1. The human problem is different only in that we have recently exacerbated and accelerated it by a dramatic improvement in human health, particularly in the care of infants.

Whether one chooses to draw a conclusion relating to the human from the equally dramatic collapse of these populations will depend more on temperament than on logic, since we have no precedent. It may be that we have only now saturated our environment for the first time; that we have reached the first peak of a set of cycles. But there is no reason to believe it except that we can see all too many signs of trouble awaiting us that are no different from those that press on the populations of other animals.

EXTINCTION

SURELY THE ONLY PREDICTABLE RESULT of population growth, indeed of biological existence, is eventual extinction. Remember the dinosaur. Of course a trivial explanation of many such population disasters is, unfortunately, an offshoot of the problem with which we are primarily concerned—man. As we shall see when we consider competitors, we have successfully extinguished many animals, are on the verge of destroying a large number of present species, and have reduced to rare, zealously protected specimens a considerable list of others. Let us hope that the human is not on someone's list.

But what actually happened to the dinosaur, the giant ground sloth, the hairy mammoth? We do not really know. The important question, of course, is whether we are headed in the same direction, and, if so, whether human extinction is avoidable or at least postponable. It is clear that many species (as the passenger pigeon) must maintain a certain population density to survive, usually because of some particular social quirk, as the necessity to defend themselves jointly against predators or to cooperate in food gathering. In this sense it is worth pointing out that the human has complicated his social structure to the point that few of us are capable of setting forth into the jungle or, for that matter, of making any effort to secure food more complicated than a trip to the corner delicatessen. Maybe the human race will end when the last man finds it just too much trouble to walk two blocks to the dymaxion house of his rosebud after his transsubstantiator blows a fuse.

It is obvious, however, that quite unlike any other species in world history, man is cognitive. We *can* foresee the possibility of population disaster or extinction. We *can* do something about it. The question is. whether we will.

26

1. / Exponential Expansion

SUMMARY

STUDY OF VARIOUS ANIMAL POPULATIONS has not resulted in any definitive conclusions about the controls that exist in nature except to show that the regulatory processes tend to be rather drastic. An interesting common feature of many of these studies is the repeated note that the animal in question suddenly seemed to appear out of nowhere in unbelievable numbers and then to vanish. We can now see that explosive increase is really the result of exponential expansion. No matter what linear scale is applied, this process is characterized by populations increasing very slowly for a long time and then shooting to incredible numbers with appalling rapidity. With the human race we have simply arrived at the point at which the numbers have become quite appreciable within the framework of our environment. Even with no further increase in rate we can confidently predict that the present doubling every thirty-five years will soon prove impossible. We can further predict that some factor or combination of factors will sooner or later control further increase. Perhaps the result will be total disaster. Hopefully we will prove intelligent enough to avoid the fate of the dinosaur or lemming, or at least to postpone it.

In the next section I will consider some of the factors that classically limit populations to see how pressing they really are on humans. It should be noted that with very few exceptions, in all other animal species control occurs by manipulation of the death rate. Man alone has the intellectual capacity to regulate his birth rate, to control population at the expense of the unborn, rather than the living. This possibility will be discussed in the third section.

27

Part II

Factors Limiting

Population

Growth

2 /

Space

There was a time, not long past, when the world was large and people were few. At that time we could and did make great blunders in our treatment of the environment without too serious consequence. If a forest were destroyed or a rangeland turned to desert, there were a thousand forests and rangelands still undamaged. Now the world is small and people are many. Serious blunders can be irrevocable. We have lost our margin for error.

— R. F. D A S M A N N, *Environmental Conservation*

THE ONE POPULATION-CONTROLLING FACTOR about which we can seemingly make the most unequivocal prediction is the limitation of living space. The earth's surface consists 71 percent of sea and 29 percent of land. The land area, including mountains, deserts, polar regions and all, is about 60 million square miles or 1.66×10^{15} (that is 1,660,000,000,000,000) square feet, seemingly an immense number. Allotting, say, one foot by two feet per person, it might seem that this amount of standing space would last forever. Alas, forever comes soon with an exponential expansion. Assuming a present population of 3.5 billion people and a doubling rate of thirty-five years, we can multiply by two to come to the conclusion that humans will be packed absolutely solid by the year 2595 or 625 years from now.

HOUSING VS. FOOD

THIS CALCULATION IS, OF COURSE, NONSENSICAL. Obviously we need more than standing room only; we must have land for agriculture, forests, industry, transportation, motels, and liquor stores. And even today space problems are cropping up. In the push for living space we are steadily encroaching on land that has for decades been used for food production. In southern California, particularly, valuable and irreplaceable truck farms and citrus groves are being swallowed up by subdivisions. One can argue that this is a necessary use of land, that people have to live somewhere. It seems singularly unfortunate that in this instance, as in a number of others, we are converting into subdivisions not land that is otherwise essentially useless, but some of our most valuable agriculture acreage. I shall return to this point when I consider food production, since what we are doing in this instance is trading one problem off against another, solving an immediate housing shortage by adding to the food problem.

WATER VS. FOOD

ANOTHER EXAMPLE is the trading of food-growing space for water impoundment. Impelled by immediate needs in many areas of the country, we are converting forest land and often high quality river bottom agricultural land into artificial lakes and ponds for use as reservoirs. (We shall consider the water problem in more detail later.) Projects of this kind seem justified by immediate need, of course, and are also attractive because they are multipurpose. They offer not only water but possibilities for recreation, tourist business, and flood control. (The last, ironically, becomes more and more of a problem as we

replace forests and fields with concrete and asphalt.) The ancillary waterways solve other pressing problems of irrigation and
waste disposal. The only catch to all of this is that there seems
to be little or no overall, long-term evaluation of our future
needs for land. Quite possibly we are doing the best thing; but
we are doing it on a rather hand-to-mouth basis—or, more exactly, on the opposite basis, since we are assiduously encroaching
on cropland.

RECREATION SPACE

WITH FAR MORE JUSTIFICATION one might question
the diversion of land into parks and recreation areas, yet as people
live closer and closer together there is a manifest need for places
where they can get away from each other a little for a few days
and see something besides concrete. Obviously the pressures
against acquisition of public lands—already considerable—will
become steadily more acute, and it cannot be long before there
will be increasing doubt that we can afford such profligate uses
of land as for parks, primitive areas, national forests, golf courses,
and recreational ponds. Yet anyone who is not convinced that
even today people really want recreational facilities of all kinds
needs only to visit Disneyland, Jones Beach on Long Island, or
Yosemite or Yellowstone Park.

Yosemite, in the summer, is not unlike Macy's the week
before Christmas. In 1965 it had over 1.6 million visitors; Yellowstone over 2 million. The total area of Federal-plus state-
owned parks is now something like 33 million acres, which sounds
impressive until it is divided by the total number of annual visitors
of something over 400 million or the present United States population of well over 200 million, far less the projected population
for the year 2000 of some 320 million. At that time, if we don't
have more park land, we shall have obviously one-tenth of an

acre of park per person. This is considerably less than the average city house lot today.

CONSERVATION

IT MIGHT SEEM that almost no one would argue against the desirability of preserving for future generations such unusual if not unique places as Death Valley, Yellowstone, the Everglades, Mammoth Cave, Grand Canyon, Carlsbad Cavern, Bryce Canyon, and the Hawaiian volcanoes. But by far the largest part of public land holdings is in watersheds, forests, and grazing lands. Even when conservationists have been able to point out that the land was essentially worthless for other purposes, local politicians have argued mightily against the Federal land holdings because of their non-contribution to local taxes. When one realizes that about 34 percent of the total land of the country *is* held by the United States Government, largely for these conservatory, multipurpose uses, it can be seen that the problem is a real one. The argument becomes particularly acute in Alaska, which is 98 percent Federal land, but important also in Nevada (87 percent), Utah (67 percent), Idaho (64 percent), and Oregon (52 percent). Nearly 90 percent of this land is in watershed, forest, and grazing holdings, only about 3 percent in parks.

It will, perhaps, astonish others as much as it did me to find out not only that 73 percent of the forest land in the United States is governmentally owned, but that the world figure is even higher (77 percent). This land, however, does *not* lie idle. Although it was acquired by the government beginning at the end of the last century to prevent total and seemingly imminent despoliation of our forest resources by commercial interests, it is mostly still in production under governmental supervision. The objective, through constant research, is to develop these resources for maximum present and future public benefit. The same is true

34

of the vast holdings of government grazing land, acquired to prevent its destruction by short-sighted over-use and now restored to usefulness by prudent management. We should also note, perhaps, that this land is *not* being withheld from useful production of food crops. Forest land and grazing land are very seldom adaptable to such use.

Obviously the pressures for increased exploitation of publicly held lands are continuous. Not only are the cattle, timber, and mining interests unremitting in their demands for exploitation, but the requirement for more and more irrigation and electrical power has threatened one after another of our most spectacular parks and reserves. Against them are arrayed such comparatively weak financially, but vocally strident conservation groups as the Audubon Society, the Isaac Walton League, and the Sierra Club. As a relatively disinterested observer it often seems to me that the touch-not-a-hair-of-this-old-gray-head of the conservationists is as unreasonable as the greed of the exploiters. Still, one wonders how long the government will be able to resist pressure against these lands as the population and its per capita demands increase.

TRANSPORTATION

ALTHOUGH IT MAY SEEM AT FIRST TRIVIAL, we must note that we are also witnessing a steady encroachment of transportation on land that previously has been otherwise used. Airports grow steadily larger and more numerous. We now have about 10,000 in the United States and of these over 2700 have paved runways. Of more than 3.7 *million* miles of highways, some 2.8 million miles are surfaced, and the distance is increasing steadily each year. Nearly every city now demands that new multiple housing units and businesses must provide parking, with the result, as we all know, that every city has enormous and rapidly increasing areas tied up in paved parking lots. All of

3 5

this makes not unreasonable the estimate that over 2 percent of the United States is now paved; a figure that sounds more impressive when stated as over 70,000 square miles or 44 million acres. Furthermore, considering that all rural highways include extra right-of-way, we may assume that we have permanently removed from other use at least double this amount of land, yet in thinking of land use one would probably be inclined to dismiss highways practically without thinking about them on the grounds that they must be a negligible factor in land allocation. Even the railroads cannot be left out since they operate on some 370,000 miles of track most of which includes right-of-way. And in a modern society we must remember that we transport power by wire over rights-of-way.

SPACE PROJECTIONS

CONCEDING THEN THAT WE HAVE MANY NEEDS FOR land that must be balanced against each other, it becomes difficult to arrive at some kind of figure that will indicate the population we may support. Looking at maps that show the distribution of various types of land usage or flying over nearly any country, it is easy to conclude that there are enormous tracts of forest, tundra, and desert seemingly totally unused by man, and it is very hard to believe that we are in serious risk of coming to an end of living space, but the figures are there. If we refer back to the examples of exponential expansion in Part I we can see why it will not take long to fill the empty space. A great deal of land, such as the polar regions, mountain tops, deserts, etc. is not foreseeably suited for almost any useful purpose with any reasonable efficiency. Even the most sanguine of optimists would find the conversion of such space a frightening prospect in terms of capital investment and time and effort required per eventually usable acre, yet the total is estimated at about 75 percent of the land area. (We shall return to this point in the following section on food production.) If one wants to make some sort of allowance for this and also for the obviously vital use of land for life support—agriculture, industry, etc.—a wild flying guess might suggest that perhaps an acre per person is more reasonable than the two square feet we used as the basis for our original space calculation. Incredibly, we shall reach this population density, at present world-wide growth rates, in 120 years. This is no distant future; it is possible that some children alive today will live to this time.

One can make this less alarming by noting that the level of one person per acre is only about two-thirds the current population density of the Netherlands. But, this tiny country utilizes not 25 percent but virtually every square foot of its area and that remains adequate only through heroic and very costly efforts to reclaim land from the sea. Even at that Holland exists largely through intensive foreign trade—at something over four times the per capita rate of the United States in 1968. Great Britain now supports—by importation of half of its food—about 0.9 persons per acre, while the United States, one of the few self-sustaining countries with surplus production, has available something over twelve acres per person.

It is easy to say that people will live more and more in sky-scraper apartments so that they can stand on each other's heads in reasonable comfort. The population density of New York City, after all, is already 21,300 people per square mile (thirty-three per acre); Hong Kong now has some 200,000 people per square mile in the urban area, one 6½ acre district of which has 1,200,000 people per square mile. I calculate this to allow twenty-three square feet per person. So a lot of compression is possible and this will free land for agriculture and industry. But the question here, as it will be with respect to every factor that we consider, is *how far we are willing to go in the direction of compromise with what we now consider ideal or pleasant or feasible or possible living.* And the danger, of course, is that we shall handle the problems compromise by compromise until we wake up some day with the realization that life isn't worth living anymore.

THE WILD BLUE YONDER

THIS SEEMS TO ME THE REAL DANGER—the fact that there seems to be an almost unlimited set of temporizing "solutions" to our problems. There are always people who are convinced that after all we can live underground or under water or reclaim land from swamps, the jungle, and the sea, or melt the polar ice caps, or some such damn fool thing. One of the pet schemes of this sort is emigration to other planets. "I mean there really is all of that space out there. We are just a speck of dust in the Universe and after all we have already gone to the moon. . . ." The fact that we know of no planet that has even the potentiality for supporting human life is no obstacle to the Pollyannas. So we will create an atmosphere for Mars, so we cool Venus from some 600°C. to a more reasonable temperature and grow algae with the carbon dioxide atmosphere until it is converted to oxygen. The ammonia and methane on Jupiter? We can set up chemical plants and burn the methane to warm the place up, maybe, etc., *ad nauseam.* Needless to say none of these proposals makes any real sense. But let's grant them. Let's suppose that Mars is sitting up there all covered with lush green pastures full of fat Jersey cows and all we have to do is get there. Brief consideration of our current exponential growth rate reveals that by the year 2059, less than a century hence, we should have to blast off 1000 space ships a day each containing 1000 people just to hold the population level at the then 18 billion. Now no doubt someone is going to say that if we can transport that many people from Flatbush to Weehawken each day now, why not to Mars in 100 years? Rather than argue the point let's move forward another thirty-five years. Since Mars is roughly the size of the earth and since in the thirty-five years we shall have emigrated one-half of the human race, the population density of Mars will be that of the earth. We shall then need two more new planets each the size of the earth or Mars and, in another thirty-five years, four more, then eight more, then sixteen. That's the trouble with exponential expansion. That's also the trouble with reclaiming land from the sea or melting polar ice caps.

The real point is that the human race, which has evolved for a million years or more—depending on what you want to call human—is now, at our present rate of growth, confronting the prospect not of another million or even another thousand years but of coming to the dead end of standing room only in a few hundred years and of being in serious trouble within the lifetimes of our children or certainly our grandchildren.

SUMMARY

ONE MIGHT ARGUE THAT, setting a firm limit on population, there is just a certain amount of dry land available for humans on the earth. Yet the fact is that we have many uses for land and an increasing tendency to trade farm land for subdivisions, open land for paved parking, public land for industrial exploitation. Unfortunately an unlimited number of compromises is, at present, possible, with the result that we continually force ourselves toward a kind of living that many now consider intensely undesirable. The question is one of when we reach the point of no return and whether we shall recognize this point only by hindsight.

3 /

Food

In general, mankind, since the improvement of
cookery, eats twice as much as nature requires.
—BENJAMIN FRANKLIN

To a man with an empty stomach, food is God.
—MOHANDAS K. GANDHI

THERE ARE PROBABLY MORE CONTROVERSIES, even among experts, about the potential for food production than about any other factor in the population problem. I have seen several statements in newspapers to the effect that some "agricultural expert" says we have not even begun to tap our food production resources and that there is no conceivable problem in the future. The "expert" usually turns out to be head of a local fertilizer plant, speaking to the Optimist Club, but never mind. The bushes are full of crackpots who talk vaguely of growing algae in the limitless sea or supporting the world forever on dried fish meal. There is some basis for such ideas, but, as usual, they simply do not take into account the nature of exponential growth. Before we look at the future we need to examine the question of how well we are feeding the people we have.

3. / Food

AGRICULTURAL OPULENCE

IN THE UNITED STATES we have just passed through an era in which we spent a considerable amount of our effort and tax money trying to cope with agricultural excesses. The storage of surplus foods and fiber and the cost of the various farm programs became a political scandal. It seemed—and I suspect that many of us find it very difficult to disabuse ourselves of these ideas—that there was no potential end to the bounty. As first marginal and later high quality land was retired from production, intensive modern farming and improved plant strains more than compensated.

Just to take a few by no means exceptional examples, the production of dairy foods rose by 24 percent in the period from 1940 to 1965, of food grain by 70 percent, of meat animals by 56 percent. Yet large scale farmers were and still are receiving government payments in the millions per farm each year to restrict production. During the same period the number of acres in cultivation dropped from 348 to 307 million while the population rose from 132 to 194 million. With an overall increase in population of 47 percent, the overall farm output rose 66 percent using 12 percent less land. This looks very prosperous indeed. The number of agricultural man-hours meanwhile dropped sensationally from 20.5 billion per year to 8.2 and the number of workers from 9.4 to 4.6 million. A record of increased efficiency and production to be proud of! But the figures that seem to catch the most attention are the fantastic increases in yield per acre. Corn, for example, in 1940, yielded an average of 26.8 bushels per acre; in 1965 the yield was 73.1 bushels—an increase of over 2.7 times.

It was very easy to believe that there was no end to this miracle. One could extrapolate to some marvelous time in the not too distant future when zero agricultural workers would

4 1

be able to produce an infinite supply of food and fiber on no land. We shall return to this point.

CURRENT MALNUTRITION

WE KNOW, of course, that this situation is nearly unique to the United States, that even the U.S.S.R., despite mighty effort, has failed to raise its production satisfactorily and that many countries fall more desperately behind each year. When we begin to consider the relationship of the human population to food supply, one of the disagreeable facts we must face is that this is not a problem of the distant future but of the past and present as well. In discussing food production, I find people again and again asking when these problems will become pressing. This despite frequent statements in the news media that somewhere between one-half and two-thirds of the world population currently suffers from hunger and malnutrition. It is also well known that when food is in short supply, children suffer first and most severely. A fairly new fact is that malnutrition of infants is not completely reversible, that permanent mental damage results. In other words at the very time in human history when progress seems to depend strongly on increased development of technical skills and on the ability to understand and cope with staggering social problems, we are severely reducing the mental capabilities of uncounted numbers of the next generation. Indian authorities have warned "that India alone is on the verge of producing 10 million intellectual dwarfs."

It is worth examining the question of dietary adequacy in a little detail. If we look at the dietary levels in various parts of the world, we find that the number of countries enjoying obesity, as we do in the United States, with an average per capita caloric intake of 3200 per day, is distressingly small. According to Brown, Bonner, and Weir in *The Next Hundred Years*, our standard of diet is matched "only by the peoples of Canada, Australia, New Zealand, Argentina, and Uruguay—who together constitute about 9% of the world population." The National Research Council of the United States has recommended 2100 calories for the average woman, 2800 for the average man, suggesting that if our present average intake were evenly distributed in the sense that the right kinds of food got to all levels of society, we would be overly well-foddered. Something over 55 percent of the human race, however, is found in the group at the other end of the scale where the average intake is less than 2200 calories. It has been argued that the Oriental is smaller and needs less food. I detect a faint odor of Candide in this rationalization, which must not be allowed to obscure the fact that in these countries, including India, Pakistan, China, Korea, the Philippines, and Indonesia, the average nutritional level is deplorable and an appreciable part of the population is at near starvation levels. A little better off is another quarter of the human race with diets at the level of undernourishment.

One must remember that caloric intake is only the simplest criterion of adequate diet and that the quality of the food tends to drop sharply along with lower total amount. High quality protein, commonplace in the United States and the other countries in the first small list, is virtually unknown in most of the world. The portion of our diet that consists primarily of starches is about 24 percent, whereas in Asia these carbohydrates constitute 74 percent of their already inadequate 2200 calories or less.

Since these facts have been given wide publicity for years, I cannot understand how presumably educated people can be unaware that in Asia and Africa *today* people are starving to death by the thousands. A recent article in *BioScience* gave a figure of 12,000 a day dying of starvation world-wide. I have seen much higher figures, if from somewhat less reliable sources.

In 1967 a well-known authority, Raymond Ewell, said that

unless an all-out effort was made by the United States to supply food, and/or unless there was a virtually miraculous relief from an unparalleled drought in the provinces of Bihar, Madhya Pradash, and West Bengal, nearly 100 million people faced an immediate future with literally no food for the remainder of that year. Incredibly the rains came, the United States did supply 149 million bushels of wheat, and disaster, though not a grave food shortage, was momentarily averted. But this will not happen every time. The food situation in India is precarious at best—one bad crop year in India or any of a number of countries could presage disaster.

At the moment the Indians are taking great heart from the demonstration of successful cultivation of a new "miracle" strain of rice, developed in the United States and yielding (under carefully supervised, intensive cultivation) "up to" five times, perhaps realistically nearer three times the amounts of rice formerly obtained per acre. Other improvements, as we shall see later, are in the offing. But from 1960 to 1967 the population of India increased from 441 to 510 million while the food production *declined* from 80 to 76 million tons. As Ewell points out, "The United States has given India enormous help in this emergency by sending 10 million tons of grain, worth about $750 million, during 1966—all virtually as a gift—and the United States will probably send 7 or 8 million tons of grain during 1967. In 1966 this was largely wheat, but now we are running out of wheat so that much of the 1967 shipment will have to be sorghum."

Food Surpluses and Distribution

It is, of course, a fact that while we have sat complacently piling up grain in elevators and butter in caves and have even frantically tried to protect surplus food from the weather by covering it in the open with tarpaulins because storage space was bursting at the seams, the people of India have been starving by the tens of thousands. But we do not need to single out the Indians. It is just that they are an enormous group that is on the edge of starvation before our eyes. Other populations all over the world are in equally bad or worse straits but less obviously so because they are dispersed in the jungles of Africa or the hinterlands and ghettoes of nearly every country—by no means excluding our own. More important, a number of experts consider the situation in India a mere preview of an imminent world famine.

Nonetheless, at the moment the world food problem is to a considerable degree one of poor distribution and economic under-development. The Communist Chinese recently revealed the seriousness of their problem by swallowing their pride—and a monstrous swallow it must have been—along with hundreds of millions of bushels of wheat from Canada. They even played footsie with the United States for more wheat. From 1960 to 1966 we sent to the United Arab Republic 20 to 30 millions of bushels of wheat per year, with mighty little thanks to say the least. But there is a catch to all of this. It was calculated, a few years ago, that the entire agricultural surplus production of the United States would supply the undernourished of the world with the equivalent of one cup of rice a week. Less than 100 calories per day, this is scarcely going to keep from starving anyone who is now doing so. But worse than that is the fact that we are rapidly coming to the end of agricultural surpluses. A spokesman for the United States Department of Agriculture stated in 1967 that our reserves of wheat, the main source of exportable nutrition, were below desirable levels for our own safety against drought or other disasters. It is also true that a large part of the starving world population would rather starve than change dietary habits to accommodate the foods we can produce and ship. Corn and sorghum, for example, are apparently a drug on the market, and much of the world's population is even quite unused to wheat. Of course the expense of shipping and distributing the food is enormous. We have found even in India, where there is a well-organized, established governmental structure, that losses of food from spoilage, rats, insect infestation, and, most infuriating of all, theft for the black market, have run some 50 percent. And finally, the food has sat upon the docks of major seaports for weeks and months while people a few hundred miles away starved to death. India—probably better off in this respect than most of the underdeveloped countries—not only lacks at the moment the ability to produce sufficient food, but to distribute adequately what is available.

I am not particularly trying to excoriate the Indians. It is true that many of their prominent politicians are quite obviously primarily interested in sweeping the problems under the rug to promote their own continuation in office, and apparently the major national political occupation is in-fighting, backbiting and scrabbling incessantly for more power. But these characteristics are far from unknown elsewhere in the world. I am citing India as an example, and far from the most hopeless, of a country where a very considerable effort to solve the current food shortage has progressed for years at a snail's pace. The political leaders in India have steadily poured money into industrialization while neglecting agriculture against all advice. At the moment of writing it appears that new "miracle" strains of rice and wheat may stave off disaster for a few years. We shall return to this miracle. The real question is whether this breather will be used to work all out toward a permanent solution.

FOOD FOR THE FUTURE

EVERY WRITER WHOM I HAVE READ RECENTLY on the subject of world food production has stated flatly that North America, as the only major food surplus area, must contribute

46

heavily to the nations of scarcity for a considerable period of time beginning immediately. At the same time we must institute crash agricultural programs in all possible underdeveloped areas. I have seen several times an estimate of twenty years as the minimum time to bring the world to agricultural self-sufficiency, but I do not know the assumptions on which it is based—whether, for instance, it includes current rates of population growth. Historically there have been two important ways of increasing food harvests: expanding the land under cultivation and improving the efficiency of the farming. Obviously both must be done as widely as possible. But exhaustive surveys have been made on the prospects with most discouraging results. The subject is enormously complex and the calculations so detailed that I can deal with it only in a cursory way.

Expansion of Agricultural Land

EXPANSION of agriculture acreage was the principal source of increased production up until 1950. During the past decade, it constituted only one-fifth of the world-wide increase. The fact is that there is little good land available for expansion. Estimates depend, as in so much of what we are considering, on how far we are willing to go, how much we are willing to spend for increased production. It seems to me, however, in the face of an exponential expansion of people, it really makes very little difference who is right—the optimists who claim that we are currently using only 80 percent or the pessimists who claim that we are using 93 percent of the acceptable agricultural land potentially available in the world.

In most of Asia, as almost everyone realizes, farmland has been at a premium for centuries. There is virtually none for expansion and in many areas the acreage available is diminishing because of waterlogging, salinity, erosion, and the enroachments of industry and housing. As we have seen, in the United States we have recently been indulging the potentially disastrous vice of converting prime agricultural land to suburban developments. In southern California, in particular, our very best land, offering the virtual optimum in terms of climate and suitability for large-scale, efficient farming, is going into housing at an alarming rate. This process is virtually irreversible, yet so far as I know no one has uttered the first suggestion that it be stopped or penalized or that agriculture be given land subsidies to stay in business. Perish forbid that we try, through taxpayer subsidy, to make farmland worth the $25,000 or more per acre than it can bring as subdivision lots. Similar shrinkage of agricultural land has been the steady pattern in Japan since 1920. In Hawaii prime farmland is now restricted by law to agriculture, but Hawaii is unique in this approach to land use.

Economics of Land Expansion

THIS points up another world-wide problem. To various extents it is possible to make the desert bloom or the jungle give way to farmland, but with what efficiency? At what cost? And to be paid by whom? Most of the undeveloped countries totally lack the capital to develop such land even where it exists in quantity—in the Philippines and Indonesia, for example. The economists calculate that we can and must put such land into production. Where else is such land available? Two popular misconceptions that should be discussed concern the agricultural potentialities of deserts and the tropics.

Making the Desert Bloom

THE PROVERBIAL MIRACLE of agriculture is making the desert bloom, with the implication that all one needs is water to make a Garden of Eden out of the Sahara. In the first place, water is not all that easy to come by in most deserts, as we shall

48

see. But there is a second problem that is even now becoming very troublesome in highly irrigated, high-production semidesert areas as, for example, those of southern California. Natural runoff water, and particularly the Colorado River water used in this area, always contains a certain amount of dissolved salts. As irrigation proceeds, year after year, the water evaporates and is transpired through the crop. (We shall discuss these facts in more detail in the section on water resources.) Much of the dissolved material remains behind in the soil, which thereby becomes more and more salty. Eventually this begins to have adverse effects on the crops, and even after only a few decades of intensive cultivation in the Imperial and Coachella Valleys of southern California this salinity is becoming a serious factor. Under ordinary conditions the increased salt concentration is carried away in run-off water during periods of heavy rainfall. This is why the ocean is salty. But in the desert such rain does not occur and the requisite run-off would be prohibitively expensive if artificially provided. It has been specifically predicted that the Imperial Valley, now supplying one percent of the United States' food, will be out of the agriculture business by the year 2000. Thousands of acres of this two and three crop a year area have already been abandoned.

It would be bad enough if this were a unique phenomenon. But the same pattern, according to Dr. C. A. Bower of the United States Salinity Laboratory at Riverside, California is as ". . . old as the pharoahs. Every early civilization that failed, failed because of the build-up of salt in the soil through irrigation." He sees this as the cause of the collapse of civilizations both along the Nile and the Tigris-Euphrates, and in Iraq, India, and much of the Middle East. The land below the brand-new Aswan Dam, he says, is already in trouble. The cure? Better water, more of it. But who will pay the price?

Unfortunately this phrase, "Sure we can do it but it will take time and cost a lot of money" is going to become a monot-

49

onous answer to our insistent neglect of the basic cause—increased population.

Tropical Paradises

AT THE OTHER END of the water scale, we find another venerable myth. As everyone knows, in the equatorial tropics, sunlight and high temperature plus ample water produce an incredible lushness of vegetation. Visions arise of a dozen crops a year of anything and everything. All we have to do is fight off the jungle that will try to outgrow our opulent produce. Well, yes and no.

The difficulty here is that indeed things grow so fast the farmer has to plant and jump back. But the plentiful rain produces exactly the opposite effect of the salinity of the desert. It washes the minerals out of the soil so rapidly that the only nutrient available is in decaying vegetation. The plant of today lives on the remains of the growth of yesterday. *Remove a crop and you remove the nutrient for the next cycle.* Remove a succession of crops and the tropical paradise will become a desert. Why not apply fertilizer? Unfortunately the rains will wash it away largely before it can be used. Is there a solution that will take advantage of the plentiful rain and year around plentiful sun and high temperature? Perhaps. But a great deal of study and research will be required and the answer is by no means assured to be favorable or economical. And so bites the dust the common idea that with a little American git-up-and-go we can hack down the jungle and feed the human race forever.

Marginal Land

IN THE UNITED STATES we have steadily reduced our agricultural acreage in an attempt to eliminate marginal, uneconomical, land-destroying farming. We can restore some or all of this land to production but at what cost and with what crop-producing efficiency? To, I must admit, a non-farmer from New England, now resident in the Midwest, it is inconceivable that the rocky hillsides of northern Vermont could compete with the great plains regardless of investment short of bulldozing New England down flat. As a Vermont vacation property owner I would be opposed. It would reduce my acreage by 30 percent and my view to zero. The current fact is that farming in northern New England is diminishing rapidly and one could perhaps argue that recreation is a far better use of this particular land. Similar statements apply to many other areas that support marginal agriculture.

We can juggle things around to some extent to improve food production. Conversion of forest land to farms sounds attractive when one realizes that forests constitute 30 percent of the earth's dry surface. But a little observation and reflection suggest the conclusion, concurred in by expert evaluation, that most forest land is quite unsuited to agriculture, and besides we need forests. It would, of course, seem reasonable to ensure optimum use of forest products. The major lumber companies already operate at high efficiency and have shown great cleverness in utilizing what was previously considered waste material. A contribution to the food problem would be made by converting the less valuable material and the huge amount of waste (about 50 percent insofar as lumber is concerned) into livestock foods, perhaps, or to nutrients for bacteria which in turn could convert the plant material into high quality food. Work along these lines is progressing, but no one anticipates that it will become a major contribution in the predictable future or even that it is really economically feasible. As Brown, Bonner, and Weir point out, *"If the need for food in the world were great enough* [my emphasis] we could theoretically convert the bulk of our woody residues to sugar or protein by this method, a measure which by itself would increase our food supply by perhaps 50 to 100 percent. The food increment would be costly, since it would require the expenditure of a great deal of energy and investment in much new technology, but it could be done should it become necessary." As with standard agriculture, however, such efficiency is practical only in the huge commercial developments. Unfortunately most of the world's forests are harvested in small operations.

Walter R. Schmitt, in *The Planetary Food Potential*, points out that using for food production one-half of the range land plus that now growing industrial crops would give a 165 percent increase in food crop land. But these improvements, obviously requiring enormous capital and causing great dislocations in our economy and eating habits (there go charcoal-broiled steaks again!), would help us only for about sixty years at our present rate of growth. Worse, extensive research has shown that grazing land is easily ruined (remember the dust bowl of the 1930's) and requires *very* cautious management.

FOOD FROM THE SEA

ANOTHER SOURCE OF EXPANSION is better use of the sea. (We shall consider later the possibility of some help from the culture of algae and from the development of processes for using "trash" fish for the preparation of protein concentrate.) As Schmitt and many others have noted, we can harvest from the sea more than we do. Unfortunately we lack the knowledge of how much of a given population of fish can be taken per year without disrupting it seriously—that is to say without altering the ecology and drastically changing the availability of future supplies. Almost everyone understands that we could surely fish more efficiently. But we most certainly want to avoid the kind of selfish, idiotic, single-minded fishing that has brought the valuable whale to the verge of almost certain extinction. We very nearly destroyed our Pacific salmon industry only a few years ago, and the Atlantic salmon industry seems headed toward severe over-fishing; it is far from certain that we can enforce adequately the rules that biologists have established for preservation and improvement of this most valuable food source. A considerable number of other sea crops are even now teetering on the edge of overharvesting because of demand, reduction of yields from pollution, and lack of understanding of the ecology and life cycles. Sardines, formerly the basis of a major industry, have nearly disappeared from the waters off California*. The fishermen prefer to believe the trouble came from mysterious changes in "upwelling" and long-term studies are under way. Despite vigorous denials from the fishermen, however, there is a sneaking suspicion that simple greedy over-fishing may be a major cause. Declines in the yields of tuna in recent years have been dramatic. Rightfully or not the blame is being assessed against Japanese over-fishing. One might also mention oysters, clams, and lobsters, just to make your mouth water. Each year more are sold and each year they become harder to get. And even where we have established conservationary regulations, it has sometimes proved impossible to enforce them, especially on fishermen from other nations. It has been claimed that the Russians are now trawling for lobsters beyond the three-mile limit of the East Coast (apparently their trawlers really do fish as well as spy) and are harvesting huge quantities of the very large breeding animals that are essential for continuation of the species. The Japanese are said to be doing much the same for crabs off Alaska. Fishermen who have traditionally scooped clams from the tidal flats of the north side of Long Island tell me that pollution is killing the clams and that every year they have to go deeper and work harder to get their limits. Alarming reports of short supply and the effects of pollution on the eastern

*The yield of sardines dropped from over 228 *million* pounds in 1950 to 69 *thousand* in 1965 to unreportable levels since.

United States oyster industry have been published repeatedly. Pollution has many ramifications and we shall return to it, but the question here is whether over-fishing—aggravated by pollution—is pushing these species in the direction of the passenger pigeon and the buffalo.

There is every reason, in short, to believe that we can use the sea better, but to do so requires huge expenditures of money, considerable time for research, and vigorous enforcement of sound natural crop management in the face of intensive lobbying by industries often concerned solely for this year's profit. We have only very recently made even the most modest beginning in the direction of thorough-going study of marine biology, and only then, ironically, largely because of rumors that the Russians were going all out in this area.

Fish Protein Concentrate

Fish, of course, we could use a lot more efficiently than we do. In a recent article in *The Sciences*, a publication of the New York Academy of Sciences, it was said that, "the seas could supply 500 billion pounds of fish annually; only about 15 per cent of that amount is now taken from the waters of the world." But before you slaver for swordfish steaks, it should be pointed out that a very large proportion of the fish that are being discussed in such statements are now not considered edible—the so-called trash fish.

We have heard a great deal in the last year or so of the prospects of feeding millions on fish protein concentrate (referred to by the cognoscenti as FPC). It is cheap, the marine biologists see a fantastically large potential supply, it is nutritious as all get-out (over 80 percent protein) and, in a fairly large pilot program, the Bureau of Commercial Fisheries has demonstrated the practicality of preparing it. They have claimed that the United States fishing fleet alone could raise its annual harvest from 5 billion pounds to perhaps 15 to 20 billion pounds of fish suitable for FPC. Apparently it doesn't even taste particularly bad— though this statement presumably comes from the fellows who are trying for additional governmental support for further study—and there seems little doubt that it could prove a most valuable supplement to protein-starved diets. Badly malnourished children in South Africa (do you want to guess their skin color?) and in Peru thrived on FPC-supplemented diets. Transportation and distribution should be fairly simple since presumably it could be made and processed on the seacoast of any country.

But although the product is described in *The Sciences* as "inexpensive" it is admitted that "there is little likelihood it would be voluntarily purchased by the people who most need it; . . . they can't afford it and, in addition, it is difficult to change the eating habits of people. . . ." In a typical bureaucratic mode of thought, "It has been suggested that various governments legislate . . . that it be included in all meals served in such institutions as hospitals, schools and military camps." In other words since this product is vaguely unaesthetic at the outset (in the interests of economy, it must come from the whole fish— blood, guts, brains, eyes, fins, scales, and all) we shall have to do a little persuading of the people we want to help. So far we have had little success in this general area of changing dietary habits, and the idea of feeding fish guts to Latin Americans, say, while we subsist on steak and turkey, is not too likely to endear us to people who already consider us pretty domineering and patronizing and who hate *our* guts, far less those of our trash fish.

Aquaculture

Cultivation of fish, mollusks, and crustaceans under controlled conditions is a promising source of high quality food. Experiments in various parts of the world show that yields of protein per acre and per man-hour are quite attractive. According to a report by Drs. John H. Ryther and John E. Bardach, summarized recently in *BioScience*,

> a ton or more of fish and a hundred tons of shellfish can be raised in the same space that it takes to raise a few hundred pounds of beef cattle. "Intensive pig farming in developed nations leads to a production per man-year of around twenty-five tons of live pigs while an oyster farmer can raise forty to sixty tons of oysters (shells excluded) per year. The average Danish trout farm produces about forty tons of trout per year, with two or three men employed to do the labor. The sewage ponds of the Bavarian Power Company, near Munich, have the capability of producing 100 tons of carp from about 200 hectares (about 500 acres) of water. Three men tend the ponds and the fish; thus the fish production per man-year would exceed 30 tons."

Another article in *BioScience* describes commercial culture of oysters as yielding 170 pounds per acre per year average, compared to the six pounds obtained from natural public beds, and suggests that yields could go as high as 5000 pounds under optimum conditions in the United States or to the 50,000 pound maximum of Japan. Shrimp, in Japan, are raised in yields of 9000 pounds per acre, under forced culture, in a period of ten months. These yields, moreover, are from a technology in its infancy with very little research on the genetics and optimization of conditions.

Before enthusiasts run wild with extrapolation, it must be pointed out that aquaculture can be done only where conditions are favorable, where shallow, *unpolluted* estuaries or lagoons are available at reasonable cost, or, with fresh water species, where large shallow ponds are feasible and ample water is at hand. It is all very well to say that it is possible to raise ten to a hundred times more protein per acre of pond than per acre of West Texas range, but scarcely practical to think of converting arid West Texas to ponds. This is no solution to the problem of world food shortage.

The experts do not, however, find it difficult to envision oysters, clams, and shrimp being cultivated intensively much as chickens are today, with very high yields per acre and man-hour and consequent reasonable prices and ample supplies to vary the diet with tasty high protein semiluxury food now in ever shorter supply. If steak has to go, let the shrimp and clam come.

AGRICULTURAL EFFICIENCY

IF WE ARE GOING TO FEED THE WORLD we must surely consider every way of getting more for our acre of sunlight than forty-three pounds of beef protein per year. This means, primarily, turning to cereals as substitutes. Yields in the United States are enormously greater, for several cereal crops, than corresponding yields in underdeveloped countries. It is all too tempting to assume that if only those ignorant, backward people would swallow their idiotic pride and let us move in with a little good old American hustle and know-how, the food problem would soon be a slightly disagreeable memory. Apparently it takes an intelligent, open-minded American agricultural expert about one day in one of the underdeveloped countries to see this problem in a slightly different way.

It is quite true that we have improved yields almost unbelievably in the United States, but we are usually speaking of crops that are suited to our climate, soil, terrain, methods of agriculture, and, never least, palates. Most of the people in the countries that need the help the worst do not want American corn or sorghum. They are also largely incapable of using our agricultural machinery. Nearly 100 percent of our boys practically from birth are right at home with anything mechanical. They teeth on Tinker-toys, graduate to Erector sets, spend the years from nine to fifteen building and repairing slot cars, and mature by mating in automobiles which they hold in a semblance of running order with sweat, ingenuity, and junk parts. The average man whom we are trying to help in the areas of malnutrition and starvation is lucky if he owns a good shovel and hoe. If we gave him an irrigation pump, he would not know with which end to plow the ground. Nor could he afford the gasoline to run it. Nor is it available if he could. Even if he were educated in the use of mechanical equipment (and that would be a long haul) and even if it were provided, what would he do with it? Much of the land is quite unsuited to mechanical equipment simply because of the terrain or small size of individual holdings. And, most of all, often he doesn't *want* to do it that way. Heresy of heresies, there is even doubt in the minds of many who have studied the people of the Far East that the basic philosophy of the region is consonant with gung-ho progress—or what we regard as progress. Perhaps it is better to be a little backward, a little hungry, but to have a little peace and quiet both inward and outward. In short, modern agricultural methods are not going to be introduced overnight. No matter the urgency.

Agronomy

ANOTHER WIDELY IGNORED FACTOR is that a good part of our improved yields has come from slow, expensive, painstaking research in agronomy. When is the best time to plant, how far apart should the seeds be set, how deep? When should one cultivate, when water? What fertilizer gives the best response for the least investment, what insect sprays should be applied, when? It is fairly easy to see that under quite different conditions of soil, climate, water supply, availability of fertilizer or sprays, much of this research must be done over or at least extended. But it will take a large number of agricultural experts and time and the results will have to be tailored to each region, each crop. Finally, of course, we have the fact that people elsewhere often prefer quite different crops whose cultivation we have not studied at all but which, taste aside, may be far better suited to the local conditions.

Raymond Ewell has recently pointed out that India now has perhaps 200 agricultural experts, mostly borrowed from developed countries and forced to learn to adapt to local conditions. This is one expert per 2.5 million people. Ewell estimates that India could use effectively at least 4000. In the United States, the Department of Agriculture has over 118,000 employees or over one per 1600 people. Even discounting those who never see dirt other than what settles on their desks in Washington, and those whose business is to *reduce* production, the discrepancy is pretty impressive. And it does not even count the large numbers in state and county organizations—for example in state agricultural colleges and universities where a large part of the agricultural and genetic research is done.

Fertilizer

WE HAVE ALSO FAILED TO CONSIDER those aspects of food production that depend primarily on a well-organized chemical industry, almost at the dead zero level in most of the countries where help is most urgently needed. Let's take India as an example again. India needs fertilizer desperately. In fact she needs it far worse than desperately. Of course it was wheat, not fertilizer, that we had to give away ten years ago to keep from drowning in it. But fertilizer, at perhaps $50 to $60 per ton ($2.50 per 100 pounds) for a good mixed type, we can produce and ship cheaper than wheat at $2.20 per bushel (about $4.00 per 100 pounds). A little fertilizer will produce a lot of rice which they like better than wheat. Rats and insects don't eat fertilizer.

How much would the use of fertilizer improve things? The answer is complicated by questions of which crop we refer to, what genetic strains of each, how much water is available, etc.

But if we operate on the assumption that farmers use fertilizer to make money, that is to produce larger crops, we can see that an enormous discrepancy exists. According to Brown, Bonner, and Weir, the Japanese use over 120 pounds of fertilizer per cultivated acre, the European farmer uses nearly fifty, we in the United States average about twenty-five pounds, while the African uses less than a pound, the Indian traditionally less than two-thirds of a pound! The average yields per acre in India are about one-quarter to one-third those of the same crops in Japan. Ewell believes that a large part of the difference lies in the use of fertilizer. New "miracle" strains of rice, now being introduced in the Orient, produce three times the yield per acre of their predecessors. But only with the application of large amounts of fertilizer.

We may hope that India is a particularly egregious example of neglect of one of the major factors that has made the agriculture of the United States, the Netherlands, and Japan so successful. The main point, however, is that throughout the parts of the world in which civilization is old, the arable soil is largely worn out. This is not to say that it cannot be restored, only that to do so will take time, money, and expert handling under the supervision of properly trained people plus proper equipment and certainly fertilizer in large amounts. Sending food may prevent immediate famine, but in the long run a far more widely based program is needed. In far too many developing countries it seems, or at least the leaders believe, that the people are more impressed with magnificent palaces, jet planes, and tanks than with such mundane things as fertilizer factories and county agents.

Pesticides

As I WRITE THIS BOOK I am frequently dismayed with the idea that it sounds more and more like *Silent Spring*, a book also written by an amateur possessed of the idea that a situation was bad and something had to be done fast. On the other hand, one could scarcely hope to write a book that caused more attention to be paid to an important problem. One would hope to avoid generalization from the extreme example and conclusions based on sentiment instead of fact. Certainly in the population problem there are plenty of starving children, crippled adults, and desperate situations to contrast with callous and venal public officials, complacent upper classes, selfish industrialists, and uninterested neighbors.

At any rate, *Silent Spring* to the contrary notwithstanding, there is no question that pesticides have saved thousands of lives, helped millions for every person killed or sickened by bad use, overuse, or accident. Not only is the control of diseases like malaria, the major crippler and killer in a large part of the world, or typhus or plague or encephalitis of great importance, but thanks to insect control, food yields have increased mightily in the technically advanced countries. Sales of pesticides topped $500 million in 1966 in the United States alone. Admitting the problems of the appearance of resistant insects, overspraying, long-lived residues, and the killing of birds and bees, it has been repeatedly pointed out by authoritative experts that our crop yields and quality would be cut disastrously if we stopped the use of pesticides tomorrow. We shall see some of the evidence when we consider the contribution of pesticides to pollution. There is reason to believe, moreover, that with so-called third generation pesticides, now being developed, the effectiveness will be raised and the danger eliminated. These chemical imitations of insect sex and development hormones will act specifically on the harmful insect and have no effect on others, far less on birds or humans. Let's give Rachel Carson credit for spurring on or at least calling attention to these developments and hope that pesticides will have a chance to play the role they deserve in improving crop yields throughout the world. If we could take the other side of the United States coin and assume that their use would raise crop yields dramatically in the underdeveloped countries, obviously it would be vastly preferable to ship pesticides rather than wheat. But, again, in the long run these countries will need their own pesticides industries, their own research men to find the correct material for local insects and conditions, their own field workers to find the best programs of use, their own county agents to spread the gospel, and, as always, capital in large quantities. None of this is going to happen overnight.

Genetic Improvements

STILL ANOTHER WAY OF IMPROVING CROP YIELDS is the development of new varieties of plants. The successes in the technically advanced countries have been phenomenal. Plants have advantages as genetic material. For one thing there are very large numbers of plant varieties in nature, and thus a great pool of genetic traits to work from. This is necessary. The geneticist seldom *creates* new qualities; he usually only reassorts existing properties into more advantageous combinations. Another advantage of plants is that it is usually quite simple to perform many genetic crosses in a relatively short time. As a result new varieties and reliable hybrid seeds can easily be selected and produced in quantity. Finally, many plants (fruit trees, for instance) are easily propagated vegetatively—that is to say by growing new plants from bits of existing ones without having to go through a sexual process. Sex is all right, mind you, even for plants, but it does complicate the selection of a useful property occurring by chance through a mutation (often called a "sport" in the older or less technical literature).

I want to remind you of a great folk hero of the early part of this century, Luther Burbank, not only because he was an American pioneer plant hybridizer, but because mention of his name raises the blood pressure of the professional plant geneticist to about 450/357. At any rate, through the work of his more scientific if less ostentatious successors, higher yields, drought and disease resistance, suitability for mechanical farming, enhanced response to fertilizer, higher nutritive value, better appearance and taste, etc., etc. have all been genetically built into one crop plant after another. A very large part of the increased yield of corn and wheat in the United States, for example, has been due to hybrid seed stocks with some of these properties. The same is true of the development of hybrid cattle, sheep, chickens, etc. Trained observers who have gone to underdeveloped countries have usually been appalled at the scrawny, low-yield animals and plants that are in general use. One reads of Peace Corps volunteers who have had great local successes just by importing a few chickens or goats that allegedly ate no more than the local animals but produced at several times the rate. Instant apotheosis—if one believes the *Readers Digest.*

At any rate there *have* been very real and important successes. Mexico, in 1944, *imported* nearly 163,000 tons of corn. In 1965, only twenty-one years later, the yield per acre had doubled and Mexico *exported* a record 1.3 million tons. Wheat presents a similar picture, going from an *import* of 432,00 tons in 1944 to an *export* of 685,000 tons in 1964, with yields per hectare increasing over five-fold. Other crops such as sugar and coffee as well as all livestock from cattle to chickens have shown great increases also. These accomplishments resulted because Mexico had a stable government dedicated to the establishment of strong programs of agricultural research which were backed heavily by the Rockefeller Foundation. Pakistan, with the advantage of the Mexican experience and Rockefeller support also, has shown parallel success in an even shorter time. Using strains of Mexican wheat and Philippine rice, developed largely through Rockefeller and Ford Foundation financing, and greatly increased fertilization, yields have increased to the point that Pakistan can begin to foresee self-sufficiency in their current Fourth Five-Year Plan despite the fact that previous plans were disrupted by a war and a severe two-year drought. India, inspired by these successes, finally began the same sort of planning in 1965–66. New strains of corn, wheat, and rice are rapidly replacing the old, low-yield strains and the Indians are most sanguine about the future of food production. Changes are occurring, but even "rapidly" has so far meant a decade or more for real improvement.

One does not need to be an alarmist, however, to note that all three of these countries—Mexico, Pakistan, and India—are near the top of the list in rates of population increase. We shall consider in more detail later the great difficulty of changing social patterns required for population control as compared to the relative ease of persuading a farmer to make more money. Meanwhile, it will be disastrous if the prospect of agricultural improvement on a large scale leads to complacency. I am afraid that many will consider the temporary amelioration of the food crisis as evidence that science will always rescue us. (It is already being referred to in popular articles as the "green revolution" that will save mankind.) The fact is that the successes represent the culmination of over a half-century of agricultural and genetic development. There will be further improvement, but no more quantum jumps of production. The geneticists, specifically, are firm in their statements that future "miracles" are not to be anticipated, whereas the present ones were throughly predictable.

We can derive, then, the conclusion that other countries *can* experience great improvements in food yields with the introduction of modern methods and particularly genetically new strains of plants. But the problem is not automatically solved for everyone. The new strains used in Mexico and Asia required years of development and adaptation to the conditions that prevail in these countries. Elsewhere they may not be considered desirable food, they may not grow well, they may prove to be susceptible to insects or disease, or unsuited to the climate or terrain. They may require unavailable fertilizer and/or pesticides. The "miracle" PR-8 strain of rice indeed gives triple the yield of former rice, but requires much larger amounts of fertilizer than has been available in India; fertilizer that is nonexistent in most of the underdeveloped countries. As has been shown clearly in both Mexico and Pakistan, a very widely based change is needed in the whole industrial-agricultural complex with adaptation to local conditions and customs. All of this requires a forward-looking stable government, capital, education, changes in social patterns, and, above all, time. Unfortunately always time, the commodity we may run out of the fastest in the face of an exponential expansion of population.

NEW FOODS

IN PROJECTING FOOD PRODUCTION FOR THE FUTURE we have seen that many factors are involved. Among other things we must decide on the food crops that will give the most human nutrition per acre and man-hour of effort and dollar invested. Unfortunately this quickly leads to critical sociological problems. Will the Indians, or Africans, or Egyptians eat the corn that we produce or go hungry first? There is considerable evidence to believe the latter. If you find this incredible, let me put a slightly more distant problem in focus.

The Alfalfa Miracle

OUR PRESENT HABITS AND PROSPERITY IN THE UNITED STATES lead us to steadily increasing consumption of animal protein. As prices at the supermarket attest, however, steak is a singularly uneconomic source of nutrition. This is partly because cattle grow slowly, require huge tracts of land on which to graze, and are expensive to ship, process, and store as market-ready food. But a more fundamental way of regarding the problem is to understand that they are secondary sources of food. The primary sources are plants, which construct food by use of energy from the sun for photosynthesis. The production of proteins, carbohydrates, and fats is accomplished only by the input of energy, and the source in the last analysis has to be the sun. Cattle consume the primary food—such as alfalfa—and rather inefficiently convert it into meat, which we greatly prefer to alfalfa. A rough rule of thumb states that each link in any food chain lowers the efficiency 90 percent. As Brown, Bonner, and Weir put it, "We feed the animal 100 calories worth of potential food for human beings, he spends 90 calories walking around and keeping warm and returns to us only 10 calories as food." Therefore, we could bolster our potential for supporting the food needs of the world enormously by much greater use of primary photosynthesis products. Perhaps we should consider eating hay.

Instead of the forty-three pounds of beef protein or the 170 pounds of wheat protein that we now recover per acre, Brown, Bonner, and Weir point out that we can produce 600 pounds of protein from alfalfa under average conditions or 1500 pounds by intensive cultivation. We have in the world huge areas of land suitable for the growth of grasses and very little else. In 1968 we grew some 125 millions tons (250 billion pounds) of hay in the United States at an average cost of something like seven to eight cents per pound of protein. Even if we have to reinforce the alfalfa protein with a few synthetic amino acids to make it the equivalent of animal protein, it is obvious that the price and potential crop are impressive. By contrast, in 1965, the United States used a lot of its grasslands for the production of about thirty-two billion pounds of total meat and the cost comparison would only make you sick. Let's just say that meat costs forty to fifty times more than alfalfa per pound of protein.

We must concede that although alfalfa has a reasonable content of protein (16 percent), the plant material is largely indigestible by humans. In addition the technologists will have to do a bit of diddling to make it look and taste like sirloin. But perhaps these are just details—or perhaps people will get pretty hungry and not care much. Like many proposed "solutions" to the food problem, this one does not seem to elicit delighted anticipation.

Algae

ANOTHER PRIMARY PRODUCT OF PHOTOSYNTHESIS is algae, raised in shallow fresh water ponds or lagoons of sea water. Raising algae is continually cited as the great white hope (actually it'll be green) for future food. Unfortunately there are several flies in the ointment. Most people who have tried the product found it pretty awful—sort of a bilious, fishy guck. Even the Japanese, who eat raw fish and seaweed anyway, were reported to have rebelled at pond algae. On the other hand some enthusiasts have proclaimed it "nutty and pleasant." In the experiments that have been done, the growth of algae proved difficult on any considerable scale under natural conditions and the cost of harvesting, drying, and preparing the product quite appreciable. Contamination with other organisms quickly became a problem, obviously demanding—as with other such examples of microbiological production as beer and cheese—a considerable degree of technical expertise for its management. The nutrients required—carbon dioxide and nitrogen—must come from somewhere and must be distributed to the algae. For advantageous production the climate must be relatively mild and persistently sunny. The capital for establishing suitable shallow lagoons and equipping them with the necessary pumps, etc. is far from negligible. Brown, Bonner, and Weir put it at ten to one hundred times the cost of preparing land for conventional agriculture. On the other hand, the most ideal algae, dried, yield some 50 percent protein of quite high quality (for a plant product). The cost estimates, like the statements about palatability, are usually colored either by the optimism or pessimism of the estimator, but a figure of five to twenty cents per pound of protein is perhaps representative, compared to wheat flour at twenty-one cents and steak at about four to five dollars per pound of protein. The yield, under good conditions, could be something like thirty-five tons per acre on a dry weight basis. This comes to 17.5 tons (35,000 pounds) of protein compared to wheat at about twenty-seven bushels or 170 pounds of protein. Producing over 200 times as much protein per acre at possibly one quarter the cost sounds marvelous until one remembers that wheat is grown in places where, by and large, water is a little hard to come by and sunlight is a seasonal thing. The notion of converting most of Kansas, Colorado, and North Dakota from wheat fields to algae tanks is also a little depressing even to one whose contact with western Kansas has come mostly from driving hastily through at the end of a hot, dry summer. One should remember that in much of our wheat-producing area even wheat can be grown only every other year because of the necessity of allowing the ground to recover moisture.

Common opinion to the contrary notwithstanding, then, the artificial, forced culture of algae would be feasible only under pretty special conditions and with enormous installations requiring a good deal of capital investment and technical skill.

Reaping algae from the limitless oceans is real pie-in-the-sky. In the first place the cells will grow only in a fairly shallow layer for the simple reason that they need sunlight and in any appreciable concentration screen it out from their compatriots below. But the real limiting factor is that sea water lacks the necessary nutrients for any appreciable growth per gallon or cubic mile or whatnot. No one has suggested how we might fertilize the sea. It has been estimated that a cubic meter of sea water (something like a ton) yields about a gram or 1/454 of a pound of plant material. Even though sea water is what we have the most of, the expenses of recovery would seem discouraging. The best way, in fact, of harvesting the directly photosynthesized plant material from the sea is the old fashioned one— let fish do it, as they will happily and for free. The only catch is that fish represent several steps of food transfer from the algae. Brown, Bonner, and Weir have estimated that at the very best the production of a pound of fish requires a thousand pounds of algae, which sentences the various creatures in the food chain to straining out at least 118 million gallons of sea water. By some estimates, this figure is low and the correct one 100 times larger. The baleen whale—a group including the largest animals the earth has ever seen—is unique in possessing the apparatus to short cut this problem. He subsists largely on small plankton and is equipped to filter enormous quantities of sea water per day. Despite this ability as one of our most efficient converters of photosynthetic activity to meat, we are busily driving the whale to extinction. Unless the unbelievable greed and short-sightedness of the whaling industry (now essentially restricted to Japan, Norway, and the U.S.S.R.) can be stayed—and every current indication is to the contrary—this most magnificent and harmless of living creatures faces a future measured in a handful of years. If the whale lived in the United States, was feathered, and flapped around making the dawn hideous with his mating cries, he might have a chance. The useless if attractive whooping crane is the object of our greatest solicitude and no little investment of time and public money. But the only hope for the whale is that he will become so rare that even the most ruthless of modern fishing efficiency will find him uneconomical.

Yeast and Bacteria

As a MICROBIOLOGIST OF SORTS I must tout the advantages of yeast and bacteria as a source of new food. They are vastly better equipped to manufacture food than either cows or artichoke farmers.* Various yeasts and bacteria will live on nearly anything

*Incidentally I hope you don't like luxury crops like artichokes. Impossibly inefficient. Fifty artichokes a year on a plant perhaps six feet in diameter? Four million ugly calories where 1500 lbs. of good solid alfalfa protein would grow. Nonsensical.

from air and water to the inedible parts of many plants (such as forest wastes) as well as sewage.

Naturally, the kind that lives on sewage battens mightily, and—good news—we are going to have plenty of sewage. They will produce high quality protein and under laboratory conditions double in number maybe every half-hour, overrunning us in joyous reproduction. Personally I find the idea of a sixteen ounce mat of charcoal-broiled, medium-rare *Escherichia coli*, representing yesterday's sewage, somewhat unappealing. One catch is that even in intensive industrial fermentation, bacteria and yeast saturate their environment at a concentration of something like a pound per ten gallons; hence the plant investment for growth and harvesting is large. Like any industrial fermentation, food culture would require skilled technical management.

The fact is that microbial fermentations have proved practical industrially, after a great deal of research, only for expensive products obtainable in no other simple way—such as antibiotics and other rare chemicals—or during times of critical shortages—such as wars. The only exceptions are those rare chemicals based on ethyl alcohol—beer and bourbon for example. Even here, were it not for the hoary superstition that the product of the distillery is superior to the alcohol made by chemists, the microorganisms could not compete in price.

Synthetic Foods

Not uncommonly, today, one hears about synthetic foods, with the implication that when we run short of food from natural sources, the chemist can create more. Like most of the panaceas for relieving the food shortages of the future, this one also has a basis. It is true that the chemist can make in the laboratory many substances that we require for food. Vitamins, amino acids (the building blocks of proteins), carbohydrates, etc. *can* be made. But for the most part the synthetic processes have great difficulty competing with agricultural or other natural sources. Two points should be stressed. One is that the chemists can convert useless or plentiful substances (as agricultural or forest wastes) into useful materials. Or he can supplement vegetable proteins with certain synthetic amino acids (notably lysine and methionine) that they tend to lack; thus making them the dietary equivalent of the much more expensive and inadequately available animal proteins. We shall no doubt hear a good deal about this sort of dietary supplementation as we come to depend more and more on vegetable foods (alfalfa?).

The main point, however, is that *the chemist cannot create something from nothing*; basically he can make food ingredients only out of something else. DuPont indeed makes nylon stockings out of coal, air, and water (if only in a quite devious sense) but they cannot eliminate the coal and air. They could replace coal with agricultural products or oil or sewage, in theory, but they must have *something* containing the carbon that is the fundamental ingredient of all organic chemicals. When coal and oil (both excellent suppliers of chemical starting materials) are in short supply and our agricultural resources are strained beyond capacity we cannot expect to turn to the chemist to pass a loaves-and-fishes miracle. Furthermore, to consider feeding the world with synthetic foods brings to mind installations that would make the DuPont layout in Wilmington look like a woodshed.

THE END OF THE AGRICULTURAL MIRACLE

SOME TIME BACK I SAID that we would return to the question of where the miracles of ever greater crop production will end. Trends so far suggest that they will not—that we can produce more and more on less and less ground indefinitely. These statistics are as manna to the Candides of this best of possible worlds. "Poor old Malthus. Little could he foresee that corn production per acre would double in the last twenty years and that PR-8 rice would triple our yield."

Like all extrapolations this notion that agricultural yields will increase without end is dangerous. In fact it is about to come right smack up against an uncomfortably hard fact. Plant physiologists, like the rest of us, became curious about the limits of crop yield, but unlike the rest of us they had a little inside information.

The puzzlement of the Bible about how an enormous mustard plant could come from a tiny seed derived from a lack of understanding of the fact that only the *information* needed to make the plant came from the seed, the rest came partly from the ground, but mostly from the air, rain, and sunlight. Van Helmont, in the early seventeenth century one of the first experimental scientists, did a fascinating experiment. He carefully dried and weighed a large tub-ful of earth and then planted a small willow tree in it. Several years later, when the tree had waxed mightily, he carefully removed it and weighed it. He then redried the several hundred pounds of earth and reweighed it carefully. To his astonishment the dirt was only a few ounces less heavy than at the outset. The tree weighed several hundred pounds. Where had it come from? Van Helmont concluded that it must have come from the water because he had added nothing else. The irony of this remarkable experiment is that the tree came from the few ounces of mineral in the dirt plus water, indeed, but also largely from the carbon dioxide which it sequestered from the air and built into a tree by photosynthesis. Ironical because Van Helmont was the discoverer of carbon dioxide gas but never suspected a connection between it and plant growth.*

At any rate, the ultimate source of plant yield *is* photosynthe-

---

*Van Helmont is also credited with having invented the word "gas." He, therefore, deserves singular acclaim as probably the only scientist in history who coined a word of three letters, instead of an eight-syllable Graeco-Latin monstrosity, to describe a discovery.

sis. Regardless of water supply, fertilizer, pesticides, genetic stock, machinery, know-how, and tender loving care, a plant cannot grow faster than it can convert carbon dioxide into the biochemical intermediates needed for growth. Carbon dioxide, though present in the air in small quantities—of which, again, more later—seems seldom to be limiting; the determining factor is energy from the sun. Now we can ask a very important question. How much plant material can we make from a given amount of sunlight? The clever plant physiologists sometime ago asked themselves just this question and discovered that under optimum conditions plants can use 5 to 20 percent of the incident sunlight. This sounds sort of inefficient, but as such things go it is pretty good; in fact we should note that it is the result of several billion years of evolution and therefore probably not to be improved on.*

Given this seeming limit of photosynthetic efficiency . . . then, how close are we to it? As reported by James Bonner in *Science,* calculation of yields of plant material per hectare or square foot or whatever have revealed a jarring fact. The agronomists, geneticists, farmers, farmers' wives, and 4-H clubbers, while possibly ignorant of this great fundamental principle, have combined to bring us to most efficient utilization of sunlight. Rice in Japan and wheat in Denmark are grown at an efficiency of 2 to 2½ percent. Several cereal crops in the United States are said to be raised with very high efficiencies, with production near 5 percent, if only under carefully supervised conditions, and during only the best part of the growing season. Efficiencies near the 20 percent limit have been obtained under idealized laboratory conditions, but even there only at the expense of a much lower yield of plant material per square foot.

---

*I say this to forestall the Pollyannas who will want to construct more efficient plants to solve all of our problems. As a clincher we should also point out that even if the efficiency were 100 percent that would serve us, at the present rate of increase, for less than 175 years.

Let us be very clear about this. Field conditions, with nonideal distribution of water, variable light, etc. are quite different. We can pour fertilizer to the plants until they are covered by it, water until they drown in it, but we will not improve the practically obtainable yield of plant material much beyond present best levels where they are limited by available sunlight. Now, of course, we can change the ratio of product to total plant in some instances. We can, for example, produce more seed (as we have with corn or wheat) per pound of leaf. The limits of this type of genetic research have yet to be determined. But the professional plant geneticists have a sneaking suspicion that we are doing nearly as well as we are likely to, at least with the major crops, because improvement of the proportion of useful product to total plant weight has been exactly the major goal of their research for some time now.

The take-home lesson seems simple. There is indeed an end to the miracle of endlessly greater agricultural bounty and it is within sight. Perhaps we can get some kind of absolute limit by taking the same nonsensical approach that we took to the space problem. If we devote the entire land surface to the growth of alfalfa and assume that the average yield will be that suggested by Brown, Bonner, and Weir for intensive cultivation, the alfalfa crop would support some 700 billion people (compared to our present 3.5 billion). Let's pass another miracle. We have already endowed alfalfa with the impossible ability to grow from pole to pole, regardless of the temperature and lack of sunlight at the extremes and from the Dead Sea to Mt. Everest despite the manifest unsuitability of much of the area for any kind of agriculture except tree growing. We have completely neglected other land uses. Why not postulate a sea crop with a similar yield and efficiency? Now we expand our output by nearly a factor of three! But the point is, of course, that even a fantasy does not help us much in the face of a population with a doubling time of thirty-five years. Far less than providing for us forever, even these ridiculous assumptions would allow us to continue only until the year 2290, a little over 300 years.

To be more reasonable, we might look at the best expert estimates. In *The Planetary Food Potential,* Walter R. Schmitt of the University of California at San Diego presents a carefully detailed analysis of the real possibilities for food production. His conclusion is that "thirty billion people ultimately may lead fairly [sic] free and enriched lives on this planet." In 1969 the "Committee on Resources and Man" of the National Academy of Sciences reported that it had "studied the ultimate capability of an efficiently managed world to produce food ... [using] all potentially arable and marginal land and an optimal expression of scientific and technological innovation, both on land and in the sea. ... Such an ultimate level of productivity might sustain a world population of 30 billion, at a level of chronic malnutrition for the great majority. [This] figure would be reached [at our present growth rate] by about the year 2075."

If these authorities are right, and my impression is that others would not want to argue too seriously, we are in trouble now and will hit bottom, in terms of barely adequate diet, in about 100 years. This is no vague and foggy future, but one that will be seen by some of our children alive today. One hundred years give us just about time to get those space ships off to Mars or to convert the entire world into one giant algae tank with people standing in it up to their chins.

SUMMARY

A CHAPTER AS LONG AND AS DISCOURAGING AS THIS ONE deserves a summary. It seems extremely unlikely that we, like Malthus, are going to be completely upset in our prognostications by some unimagined developments. Too many people have tried imagining. Lester R. Brown, a well-recognized authority of the United States Department of Agriculture, concludes each of his two large reports (*Increasing World Food Output*, 1965 and *Man, Land, and Food*, 1963) with gloomy statements along the lines— by no coincidence, since they represent most expert opinion— that we have developed: "The prospects for many of the less developed countries are not good.... many... will find it difficult to arrest the downward trend in per capita food output in evidence over the past few years." "The ability to raise yields per acre is closely associated with the level of development." "The rapid growth in the need for professional agricultural workers... in the less developed regions, may result in a world-wide shortage...." "Food shortages... are a sympton of.... unprecedented rates of population growth... in almost every less-developed country." "Arable land per capita is declining in every region." "... the less-developed world is steadily losing the capacity to feed itself." Brown, Bonner, and Weir in *The Next Hundred Years* talk mainly about our eating alfalfa and see no great problem in that time if we do. I cannot decide whether they are kidding or not. Many people see salvation in the "miracle" rice and wheat strains being introduced in various areas, but the respite from oncoming famine will prove short indeed unless population growth is controlled.

The point, of course, is that there are limits to food production and that feeding a population that is doubling every thirty-five years will force us—well within the lifetimes of our children— toward heroic measures, enormous expense, and compromises with our standard of living that now seem quite unacceptable. Man, the supposedly rational animal, is seemingly preparing to face a future of grim prospect at the best rather than try to make rational decisions now about the numbers of people this planet will support under conditions that are comfortable, not merely less and less tolerable.

3. / Food

Most incredible of all is our apparent unawareness that food problems are not a cloud on some distant horizon but a fact of life right now, with over half of the world malnourished, thousands literally starving each day, and the possibility—by some estimates —of global famine within a decade.

4 /

Water

Pure water is the best of gifts
That man to man can bring,
But who am I that I should have
The best of everything?

Let princes revel at the pump,
Let peers with ponds make free.
Whiskey or wine or even beer
Is good enough for me.

—Attributed to LORD NEAVES

WATER IS SOMETHING that comes out of the faucet. Anywhere. Everywhere. You can drink it, wash in it, water your lawn with it. It puts out fires, floats boats, carries sewage away, grows fish. You can swim through it, sail on it, or drown in it. Ball point pens and watches work while immersed in it. As ice, water performs even more splendid services such as cooling your whiskey and then assuaging the headache it gives you. As steam it heats houses and drives turbines to provide electricity. It falls out of the sky for free. Good old water.

One could go on almost endlessly extolling the virtues of this most plentiful substance on earth.* The only difficulty is that we take water so much for granted that it is nearly impossible to believe that we really have water problems right now, even in the United States. The real predicaments, however, are still on the horizon and, as with many other aspects of the population problem, when they arrive it may be too late to escape from them.

There are, of course, very large areas of the world where usable water is a rare commodity right now. The deserts and tundras, which constitute 6 percent of the total earth surface, are so deficient in available water that little or no life can be supported. The regions of perpetual frost, where water is essentially unavailable for life processes, contribute another 6 percent. At the other extreme are the oceans, comprising approximately 71 percent of the total surface and offering unlimited water but in a form unusable to land creatures. In all, then, major water problem areas comprise about 83 percent of the earth's surface. Paradoxically, the facts I have just listed make it immediately quite apparent that we do not, in general, suffer from a lack of water. We suffer from severe maldistribution, and, in one sense, from an embarrassment of it in forms that are relatively useless to us, occupying space we could well use in the future for living or agriculture. Melting the polar ice caps, it is often said, would raise the sea level some 100 feet. Obviously this represents a fantastic amount of water even if obtainable at the expense of the tourist business of Florida (almost all of which would be under the waves). Furthermore the polar ice is fresh water. The fact is that we have plenty of water, the problem is getting it where we want it when we want it in usable form at a feasible cost.

Although water problems either of surfeit or paucity, or their

---

*To be picky, water is really pretty rare compared to the total bulk of the earth. But it is the most plentiful substance "on earth"—that is in the thin film of the outer surface that supports life.

uncontrollable alternation, are traditional in many areas of the world, the main difficulties with which we shall be concerned are those that spring from increasing population and increasing industrialization and urbanization. We shall consider mostly the United States since it is mainly here that the problem has been at least partially studied, and therefore we can here see clearly examples of the difficulties of the future for us and for the developing world. The related problems of pollution will be considered in the next chapter.

WATER RECYCLING

WATER IS A PECULIAR RESOURCE in that, unlike coal or oil, it is not really consumed; instead it cycles fairly rapidly through animals and plants, streams, lakes, oceans. Of course in the last analysis nothing is really consumed. Petroleum, for example, is taken from deposits in the earth, refined, burned and thereby converted into carbon dioxide and water. Goodbye petroleum. But no. The carbon dioxide in the atmosphere is available for plant growth through photosynthesis and under the right conditions these plants could die, decompose, and, in the course of millions of years, conceivably again form petroleum to be burned by future profligates. Copper is mined, made into electrical equipment, and hence removed from further use seemingly. But again no. Some 40 to 50 percent of present copper comes from reclaimed material, and a similar situation obtains with iron, gold, etc. So the only real difference is that the water cycle may be quite short while the petroleum cycle is infinitely long from the viewpoint of the human race. The total amount of water on earth has, in essence, been constant for billions of years, at least since the time of the appearance of the most primitive life. It varies only in form (steam, water, ice, or chemically bound) and distribution. When we talk about water resources, then, we are really talking about the speed with which usable water recycles to any given place and whether the recycling is keeping up with the rate of depletion in that area.

HUMAN WATER NEEDS

IN THINKING ABOUT THE WATER NEEDS OF A HUMAN, it is tempting to say that the amounts being discussed are really trivial, that the numbers of humans for any forseeable future are utterly negligible compared to the bulk of the sea (about 354,000,000,000,000,000,000 gallons) or even the fresh water content of the Antarctic ice cap (perhaps some 23,000,000,000,000,-000,000 gallons). After all, a human needs only about two quarts a day for drinking and it is at first blush apparently reasonable to assume that if he had a bit more for brushing his teeth and a weekly bath out of a wash basin he could get along pretty well in a pinch. We are all well aware, of course, that we bathe a good deal more than that and that a shower or bath tub uses a lot more than a sponge bath. And, needless to say, the family clothes washer uses a fair amount as does the garbage disposal. Flushing a toilet is pretty wasteful, and we have to admit that washing the family car and watering the lawn may make the total add up, but, after all, the average family, even with all of these activities, uses only about ten thousand gallons of metered water a month—something under 100 gallons a day per person. But 100 gallons already seems a long way from the two quarts we began with! Perhaps we *should* be a bit less prodigal.

Before we take alarm at this jump of 200-fold over our original rock bottom estimate of human needs, we might note that rainfall over the United States provides nearly 5,000 *billion* gallons a day! Dividing this by our 100 gallons daily per person suggests that we have in the United States alone enough water for 50 *billion* people even at our present exorbitant rate of consumption. Alas. It is this sort of common sense figuring which leads to comforting ideas that we can go on forever. We have left out a few rather troublesome factors; the water experts come up with quite a different answer.

Transpiration Water

MANY REPORTS CONCERNED WITH THE UNITED STATES WATER resources have appeared in recent years. Almost all that I have seen come to about the same conclusion—trouble is just around the corner. In a much quoted article in *Science*, a journal read each week by tens of thousands of practicing scientists, Charles C. Bradley offered some rather discouraging but typical figures. We tend to forget that man needs not only water but food and that the production of food takes water. Bradley, using a diet of wheat as a minimal example for illustration, suggests that we may assume, world-wide, an average daily dietary requirement of 2½ pounds per person. When any plant grows it draws water from the soil to build into plant material (which is over one-half water), but additionally it *transpires* a very large amount of water. (Transpiration refers to the water that is withdrawn from the soil by the roots, passes through the plant, and is evaporated from the leaves in the course of plant growth.) Wheat has a transpiration ratio of 500, which is to say that by the time a single pound of wheat plant is ready for harvest the plant has transpired (in essence, used) 500 pounds of water! Since the usable wheat grain from the plant constitutes only about half of the weight of the plant, we must double this, even, to reach a figure of 1000 pounds of water per pound of wheat grain ready for consumption. On our assumption of 2½ pounds of wheat a day per person, then, we must add 2500 pounds or some 300

8 2

gallons of water to the two quarts we were allotting ourselves for drinking. Obviously we are not going to help this much by economizing on brushing our teeth.

But this is only the beginning. As we have commented previously, in the United States we much prefer a diet that features meat and hence is much more costly in water use. In addition, we use paper, dress in cotton, wool, and other fibers, smoke tobacco, drink beer, and keep cool with air conditioning. These must all be taken into account.

To do so Bradley next assumes a daily diet containing the animal fat and protein equivalent of one pound of meat and two pounds of vegetable foods. This may seem generous compared to our per capita *direct* daily consumption of slightly less than one-half pound of meat, but when one includes poultry, eggs, milk, milk solids, butter, and cheese the estimate does not really seem excessive. Similarly the sum of all vegetables and fruits is clearly near two pounds per day per person. We already have seen that the vegetable part of this diet would require about 240 gallons of water per day to produce. When we consider the animal part, however, we see again why the American diet is so exceptional, why beef is so expensive, and why many experts are already mumbling that the days of the charcoal-broiled steak are numbered. I can do no better than to quote Bradley:

A mature steer consumes between 25 and 35 pounds of alfalfa a day and drinks about 12 gallons of water. Alfalfa has a transpiration ratio of 800, hence 20,000 pounds of water are required to bring [this] 25 pounds to maturity. . . . It takes about two years to raise a steer. Distributed over the two years, [he gains] one pound of meat per day. . . . *In other words [20,000 pounds] a little over 2300 gallons [of water] per day per man are required to introduce 1 pound of beef . . . into a person's diet.* [My emphasis] Add to this the 200 gallons necessary to round out his diet with 2 pounds of vegetable matter and we have a total water requirement of about 2500 gallons per day for a substantial American diet. . . . It should be remembered that these are conservative figures, because transpiration rates are derived from carefully controlled laboratory experiments and not from data collected in the field where perhaps half the total rainfall is lost directly by evaporation and does not pass through the plant body.

Bradley has also not mentioned the frequently cited fact that about 35 percent of our food is lost through spoilage and waste. It is not clear to me whether this factor is taken into account in Bradley's two and one-half pound diet or the United States Department of Agriculture's "annual consumption" figures; in the interests of conservative estimation, let's assume so.

Nonfood Use of Water

Now that we have man fed, it seems desirable to clothe him. The average yearly consumption of cotton in the United States is about twenty-six pounds per person. Not all of this goes into clothing, of course, but at least it isn't eaten so we must add it to our water use. Published data yield a figure of about 100 gallons of water per person per day in the United States to provide us with cotton. Wool, another nonedible commodity, is used in the United States at the rate of about two pounds of cleaned wool per person per year. Even though this is less than one-tenth of the cotton consumption, the wool comes from an animal, which is to say that it is one step up the food chain removed from the original source. A rough calculation suggests that it takes 300 to 500 gallons of water a day per person to provide even this quite small amount of wool. Tobacco, of course, is a major crop that is not eaten. The annual per capita consumption of 11.5 pounds requires something like twenty gallons of water per day. This may sound trivial compared to the by now staggering human per capita total, but it seems to me a little surprising if put on the basis that we smoke up over forty times as much water as we drink or a fifth of our daily household use. Considering the huge amount of grain that goes into alcoholic beverages at 18.5 gallons per person per year, it seems likely that we also drink a lot more than we drink. J. R. A. McMillan of the University of Sydney uses a figure of 300 gallons of water to produce a pint of beer in Australia. This comes to about 120 gallons of water a day per person for beer alone.

If we want to educate the man, provide him with his daily newspaper, and fill his mail box with trash mail, we must take into account his daily consumption of 1.2 pounds of paper. Trees grow slowly and have an enormous leaf surface. So far as paper and lumber production are concerned the leaves, limbs and bark, constituting about 25 percent of the total tree-mass, are waste. The best figures that I can find (and these are, by the nature of forests, very rough) suggest that some 200 gallons of water per person per day is needed to produce our paper. We must also add the per capita lumber consumption of 0.61 board feet per day. This would presumably require about another 150 gallons of transpiration water.

Air Conditioning

ONE MORE RAT HOLE down which huge amounts of water now disappear is provided by air conditioning. Your window unit depends on the outside air, no matter how hot, to cool the compressed refrigerant whose expansion inside your house cools you. In commercial air conditioning, however, cooling by air would require far too large an installation, so water is used. It seems singularly unfortunate—if obviously inevitable—that air conditioning is needed heavily in the United States in the region south and west of the Rockies, exactly where water is scarcest. I have not been able to find an estimate of the water used in air-cooling, but it is said to be a very large amount.

Industrial Use

IF YOU ARE READING WITH ALARM, at this point, please note that we have scarcely broached the subject of industrial uses of water. To cite only a few important examples, it takes some 270 tons of water to make a ton of steel, 1400 tons per ton of rayon, 4700 tons per ton of synthetic rubber. Total industrial usage was estimated for 1965 at over 60 *trillion* gallons. This amounts to another 850 gallons per person per day.

Putting all of this together we come to a total per individual (in 1965) of over 5100 gallons a day. Please note that this figure represents *accountable* used water.

Water Use in the Future

WHEN WE TRY TO MAKE PROJECTIONS, we must, of course, note the very heavy per capita increases during this century. As Fig. 5 shows, estimated usage of measured water is increasing almost unbelievably as we industrialize and urbanize.

The exact shape of each of these curves is arbitrary, being determined by the units used on the vertical axis. As can easily be seen, however, the use of water *per person* has increased more than three-fold during a period (1900–1980, est.) in which the population increased about 2.4-fold, yielding *a total use increase of eight-fold*. The projections to the year 1980 are based on the assumption of a levelling off of the increase in use per capita and are probably therefore conservative if past experience is any guide. They nonetheless suggest a use of metered water by 1980 more than ten-fold the use at the turn of the century.

Please note that the figures on the graph do not include water for the nonirrigated part of our American diet. As we have already pointed out, inclusion of this transpiration water would raise the present total to about 5100 gallons per person per day, nearly three times the measured use.

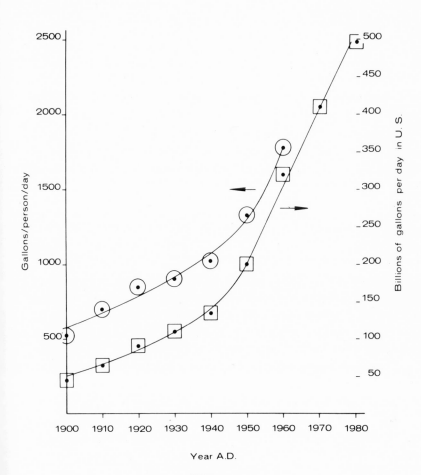

FIG. 5
MEASURED WATER USAGE
IN THE UNITED STATES

Water Resources

Beginning with the notion that a man could get along with perhaps two quarts of water a day for drinking we seem to have come a long way in water use to provide ourselves with present day amenities and diet. The question of how much water it takes to keep an average United States citizen afloat is important, of course, only in terms of how much water is available. We have already commented on the fact that the main problem, at present, is distribution—that if we could really bring the water of Canada and the Pacific Northwest to the area west and south of the Rockies we would have licked a large part of our current problems of maldistribution. But what of the future?

I hope that the discussion so far makes it evident that the consumption of water is very much related to the population. Food production, a factor that is intimately tied to the population and its standard of living, requires over half the accountable usage of water. What we really want to know, then, is what kind of limit water resources might put on population. Again, we shall concern ourselves only with the situation in the United States, because it is the best studied. Charles C. Bradley, in the *Science* article previously mentioned, suggests an alternative way of calculating water use against resources. Instead of trying to account for the water we know we use, he subtracts from the total the water we *do not* use. It is generally agreed that the average rainfall in the coterminous United States is about thirty inches per year or about 5000 billion gallons per day. This sounds enormous, but represents only 25,000 gallons per person per day. In other words *our current level of usage is incredibly about 18 percent of the total rainfall* even on the basis of the figures derived above for directly accountable use.

Needless to say, we cannot use all of the rainfall. The discharge of our rivers accounts for about one-fourth of the total. On the assumption that the continent is essentially at equilibrium with respect to water, the remainder must be returned to the atmosphere as either evaporation or transpiration. Expert opinion suggests that this 3700 billion gallons per day or 18,500 gallons per person per day is probably about evenly divided between the two. Transpiration water, you will remember, constituted a very large proportion of the daily human requirement for food; the total available of about 9300 gallons per person per day must be compared to our estimate of about 3000 for the current production of useful plant products. We are, in other words, far from a comfortable situation; at the moment we can *account* for the use of one-third of the transpiration water. Obviously we cannot double this use each thirty-five years for very long.

We should now look at the evaporation water, some 1850 billion gallons per day, essentially wasted so far as human use is concerned. Granting that this huge amount of water should be returned to the atmosphere to maintain the present cycle, it would be far more desirable if it could do so through transpiration or otherwise usefully rather than through evaporation. But now we return to the point made in the discussion of food, that, in essence, we are right now using for food, fiber, and wood production essentially all of the land that is suited to these purposes. It does not seem likely that we can increase the transpiration greatly. This is especially true when one considers Bradley's statement that some 2 percent of the United States is now paved and another 2 percent is devoted to parks and wilderness areas. As we occupy more and more of the surfaces with roads, parking lots, buildings, reservoirs, hydroelectric-irrigation lakes, irrigation canals, and swimming pools the amount of water that goes into largely useless run-off and evaporation steadily increases. A considerable amount of land has also been made unproductive by bad agricultural management. We can hope that some of this wasteland can be retrieved. In all, Bradley estimates that perhaps 10 percent of the land in areas where the rainfall is quite adequate for agriculture is now nonproductive.

Three-fourths of the nation's rain falls on about half of the nation's area, and it is this three-fourths, largely unmetered, that does the big job of raising crops for America. Subtracting the perhaps one-tenth of this rain which falls on unproductive areas and about one-fourth as unconsumed run-off, we have a remainder of about 2500 billion gallons per day which we are *consuming*, though perhaps wastefully, to raise our crops. . . . This amounts to approximately 13,800 gallons per day per person. . . . Adding the previously cited meter use gives a grand total [requirement of] 15,200 gallons per day per person. . . . At [this rate] *we seemingly can accomodate 50 million more people, or a total population of 230 million before our standard of living starts to suffer. There is little doubt that America will have reached that population well before the year 2000* [my emphasis].

We now have two figures for water consumption. The earlier one of 5100 gallons per person per day, based on laboratory conditions for the raising of plants, is a minimum required to maintain our present standard of living. Since most of this consumption is for agriculture, any substantial reduction must come from improvement in rainfall management in the field. Bradley's figure of 15,200 gallons per person per day represents our present rate of *actual* consumption, in the sense that we are allowing much of our water to evaporate or transpire under far from ideal conditions. The difference between the two figures represents additional water *available* to us if we husband it under laboratory-like conditions in our general agricultural practice. This seems like a tall order, particularly when we note that the difference between the two is only a factor of 3.5 and that the present rate of population growth in the United States implies that we shall need to attain the idealized water husbandry within the lifetimes of our children in order to maintain present dietary production.

In addition to population growth, of course, we must also consider the steady drive toward improvement of the American material standard of living. As we all know, there are vast differences between the lives of the urban, air-conditioned, meat-fed middle and upper classes and the quite considerable fraction of our population that lacks these perquisites. Our current attempts to eliminate poverty and improve the general national standards of living can do nothing but increase food and water consumption per capita. We are increasingly shifting to a meat-heavy diet, for example, and the addition of a piddling one ounce of meat per day to the average diet would increase per capita daily consumption of unmetered water by about 150 gallons or half again as much as the present metered household use.

I have gone into such detail on the water problem to try to make more believable to you a statement that I found quite inconceivable at first—that we are even now seriously pushing the limits of water supply. A presidential Select Committee on Water Resources several years ago reported that their best estimate was that by the year 2000 we should be directly consuming 18 percent of all of the rain that falls on the United States and that this is about the limit in view of the water that evaporates, runs off, and is needed for the carrying away of wastes, the generation of hydroelectric power, and the maintenance of our waterways. Since even our by no means complete estimates cited above suggest indeed that we are now using some 18 percent, the figure of the commission seems to me, at least, by no means as unbelievable as it did at first. It is also true that most projections by experts have tended steadily to err on the side of conservatism.

Stored Water

LAKES AND RESERVOIRS, by and large, are the immediate sources for metered water. In general they depend on yearly rainfall for replenishment, and it is a rare city that has available more than a few months' supply of locally stored water. We have had numerous instances of depletion of such stocks because the population has outgrown the buffer capacity of reservoirs. One of the most dramatic occurred because of the New York City drought of 1965. Even in retrospect it is difficult to know whether to laugh or cry at this serious but incredibly ludicrous situation. The city reservoir system had been designed to withstand a two year drought—unfortunately the 1965 near-disaster resulted when the drought stretched to four years. Confronted with a really dangerous situation, the first admission was that the city had never metered the water and had no knowledge of where it went in what quantities. Huge water mains were found to be gushing full into drainage ditches as the result of breakdowns that had existed for years. Incredible estimates were made of the amounts being lost by leaky taps—after all why repair them when you weren't charged for water use? Emergency laws forbade restaurants from serving drinking water. Hertz and Avis stopped washing their cars; Tiffany's filled a window-display fountain with gin. A downpour in the region feeding one reservoir went for nought—the bed was so dry it had cracked and all the water ran out the cracks. And all the while the Hudson, one of the country's major streams, flowed majestically by, so polluted as to be utterly useless.

Far more serious—now that New York is for the moment water solvent— is the situation in the Great Lakes region. The greatest single source of fresh water in the world, containing the equivalent of over three years' rainfall for the entire United States, these lakes are dropping in level year after year. Lake Erie and Lake Huron have dropped five feet in twelve years.

"Lakeside" cottages in some areas now face acres of mud flats. Docks are a quarter-mile from the water. The situation in the larger lakes, Michigan and Superior, is said to be following close behind. Representative Jim Wright, in *The Coming Water Famine*, points out that each one-foot drop represents 20,000,-000,000,000 gallons of water or an eighty-five day supply for the entire country. And it should be pointed out that the situation, unlike that in New York, does not represent the result of a disastrous drought but simply the yearly deficits accumulating from supplying the surrounding population which is currently growing as rapidly as that of any major area in the country.

Ground Water

So far we have talked only about the cycling of the annual rainfall and surface storage of water. As we all know, historically an important additional source is from wells, particularly in arid parts of the world. In some places these aquifers (water-bearing soils) go down a thousand feet or more and contain vast amounts of water that have been stored over the ages. Many important communities in the United States depend largely on ground water. One might name Houston, Tucson, and Phoenix as typical examples. Almost without exception, it was found in a recent congressional survey, these communities are finding it necessary to go deeper and deeper each year. In Houston the water table is dropping at the rate of some eight feet a year. In Tucson they are finding it necessary to go about seventy feet deeper than seventeen years ago. Local authorities are of the opinion that they can go to 300 feet and that the water will last the *present* population for 135 years at the *present* rate of consumption. Unfortunately, neither of these factors shows the slightest signs of holding still for them. The end of this exhaustible resource seems clearly in sight in a number of important centers of population.

Representative Wright reports that the survey by his committee revealed concern over dropping water tables in seventy-two of ninety-seven replies from the 105 cities of populations over 50,000 depending largely on ground water.

IMPROVING THE EFFICIENCY OF WATER USE

THERE HAVE BEEN, of course, many suggestions for improving water use. Replacement of flush toilets with more economical units is a favorite, but surely by now the possibly thirty gallons a day per capita for flushing seems pretty trivial. Much more important is the reuse of industrial water. It was reported in *Science* magazine that 94 percent of industrial water is used for cooling and could be recirculated fairly easily with small loss. Unfortunately we have set up our plumbing on the assumption that used water is used water; to separate everywhere chemically and biologically contaminated water from water that has just flowed around a stainless steel tank for cooling would be a tremendous undertaking. Many cities in the United States are now confronted with multimillion dollar storm water drainage projects, not so much to conserve water, but to relieve intolerable loads on sewage treatment plants. Clearly it is in the area of run-off water that we can hope to make the most unequivocal progress. No one lobbies against using it. Flood control and irrigation dams offer the possibility of saving much of the run-off or at least of evening out the flow in rivers. Unfortunately at the same time we pave more ground, cut down more forests, and by most of our progressive enterprises *increase* useless run-off. It is difficult to say whether we are winning or losing.

A paradoxical aspect of this situation has been pointed out in recent arguments over the dams proposed for the Colorado River. Conservationists—with quite another axe to grind—claim that the impoundment of water, far from conserving it, exposes

94

it to evaporation in vast shallow lakes in an area where temperatures are high and humidity low. The net effect, they claim, is to *reduce* the local water supply by converting potentially useful river water into lost evaporation. I have not seen an evaluation of these claims and counter-claims by a disinterested expert, but the literature is currently full of research on the reduction of evaporation from open water by the application of very thin floating layers of various chemicals—which sounds to me suspiciously like polluting it.

We can do little about most evaporation except to ensure that as much of available land space as possible is occupied by useful plants. For some crops, a practice of covering the ground with plastic is recommended to reduce weeds and evaporation. It is hard to conceive of this on a scale of a million acres, but who knows? Agricultural experts are not sanguine on this score, as we have noted already. It might seem nice if we could reduce transpiration. Some types of desert plants are very clever at conserving water. If we could cross a cactus with alfalfa, perhaps we might accomplish miracles. After all, Luther Burbank (just to make the plant geneticists mad again) tried seriously to cultivate prickerless prickly pears as cattle food. His mantle has, however, not yet been taken up by anyone I have heard of. It is largely true that decreasing transpiration would *increase* evaporation and run-off.

Shortening the Cycle

Flush twice, Dallas needs the water.
  —Graffito in Fort Worth, Texas, men's room

SOME TIME BACK I commented on the fact that water is not really used, it just goes around and around in longer or shorter cycles. If you have lived in St. Louis, as I have, you can become acutely aware of the fact that every drop of water you drink is largely second- or third-hand. It comes out of the

Mississippi and it goes back into the Mississippi. The folks up at Hannibal, Keokuk, Des Moines, and Bismarck have all had a crack at it first. Not to mention the taxpayers of Chicago. The only polite question is whether they have returned the water to us in aesthetically pleasing form, and this is the subject of our next discussion—pollution. Nonetheless, the faster we can make water go around, the better. The water of the Ohio River is said to be used 3.7 times on its way to the Mississippi. One could argue that in the interests of shortening the cycle, we should let no fresh water run into the ocean. One can assume that the farmers of the Mississippi delta might object vigorously to having the father of waters reduced to a trickle. We tend to forget that rivers provide the means of important transportation—that we now have 25,000 miles of navigable waterways carrying 10 percent of all freight. In theory, however, there is no reason that I can see why a city could not take its water from a lake or reservoir, use it, clean it, and return it to the reservoir minus only transpiration and evaporation. Then at least we would be using our *own* second-hand water.

It is too great a temptation to tell a story—probably apocryphal—that was going around microbiological circles a year or so ago. It seems that our astronautical heroes had been briefed on dangers from rocket explosion, mechanical failure that would leave them stranded in space, suffocation because of meteorites puncturing their capsule, probably even attacks by bug-eyed monsters. They had accepted all of this with the dauntless bravery that we have come to expect of the flower of our youth. But when they were told that on a long trip they would have to reuse their sweat and urine, an initial reaction of absolutely unbelieving horror was soon replaced by one of resolute revulsion and refusal. It was carefully explained that the water so reclaimed would be pure far beyond anything they would get out of a faucet on earth. No taste, no smell, no color, no germs, just beautiful pure H_2O. No sale. The argument is said to have gone to the highest levels before a compromise was reached. With the assurance that the entire space program would have to be scrapped otherwise, our heroes agreed—on the sole and absolute proviso that there would be separate (but equal?) facilities for each man who would drink only his own reclaimings.

At any rate, it is obvious that such local reuse is well within the capability of present day water and sewage treatment. If people could be prevented from watering their lawns and gardens, washing the family car, and spraying water into air-conditioning towers, the supply could go round and round happily with only a fairly small loss probably replaceable almost anywhere by rainfall. It has even been suggested that the family could—in the future—constitute a water unit, with recirculation, purification, etc., right in the home. Except for the considerable expense of installation and operation there seems no real barrier to this notion. I would guess, however, that the average American citizen of Cairo, Illinois, even more than the astronaut, would rather cling to tradition and take his water from the Mississippi, closing his eyes (and nose) to the fact that it is reprocessed Chicago sewage and industrial waste, tastefully diluted with a bit of rainfall and delicately flavored with a dash of run-off from the barnyard and a soupçon of St. Louis spent beer liquors. The most advantageous aspect of closer recycling of metered water is that the process allows expansion of water use *without* water import or expanded storage, and hence contributes greatly to the most serious problem of maldistribution.

But in all of this, we must look again at our figures for water usage. Since clearly the major part by all odds is transpiration water from food production, it is obvious that sewage recycling even at a fantastic clip is not going to answer our overall problems for long. If 3300 of our total daily per capita use of 5100 gallons is imported to the city in the form of food, no amount of local familial and industrial recycling is going to help. Water shortage in the long run is food shortage.

Desalination

Water, water everywhere
Nor any drop to drink.
——Coleridge

EVEN WITHOUT THE FIGURES about the volume of water in the oceans, it does not take technical knowledge to see that therein lies an apparent solution to water problems for all time. This idea has been fostered, recently, by a considerable amount of publicity describing attempts to produce acceptable fresh water by removing the salts from sea water. This publicity, almost by definition, comes from people who are hoping for more financial support for research, hence they tend to gloss over a fact that more disinterested observers have stressed again and again. Water from the sky, impounded in lakes and reservoirs or flowing by in streams and purified for public consumption, can be sold for about one to three cents per 1000 gallons depending on the volume of the operation, the distance over which it must be transported, and the use for which it is intended. Irrigation water is generally priced at this base level; in fact it *must* be in order to produce most foods competitively. The price to large industrial users is usually about twelve to twenty-eight cents per 1000 gallons. Water metered to the home owner costs something like twenty to sixty cents per 1000 gallons. (A glance at my current water bill shows a unit price of eighty-eight cents for water that comes from reservoirs about fifteen miles away. This price, however, is mainly a tribute to local mismanagement.) In evaluating these figures and comparing them with prices of desalinated water two things must be kept in mind. Water prices often reflect a considerable tax subsidy either concealed or direct. Reservoirs constructed with tax money are often largely charged off to flood control, power production, or recreation. Few large water developments at the local level are today constructed without a major federal tax contribution. All of these water rates, moreover, are *delivered* prices, whereas desalinated water is invariably priced *at the plant* despite the fact that distribution generally accounts for about three-quarters of the consumer's cost. The high cost to the homeowner consists very largely of expenses of treatment and delivery.

The basic fact, despite the vagaries, is that water from the sky is available for the major use of food production at a price of perhaps two or three cents per 1000 gallons. Calculations for huge, nuclear-powered, combination electric power-desalination plants suggest a comparable price of about twenty-five cents per 1000 gallons. Projections of nuclear power enthusiasts suggest that *eventual* developments might lead to a by-product water price *at the plant* as low as fifteen cents, more than five times that of natural water. No one, apparently, is considering anything lower. In addition it must be noted that we are talking in terms of huge installations—hundreds of times larger than any now operating— in order to achieve these economies. It is estimated that such plants might produce over 600 million gallons of water a day.

But water distillation on this scale raises a number of serious problems. The first, of course, is how to distribute the water. It is a long haul from the ocean to Dodge City. I have not read any proposal to distribute desalinated water on any wide scale to other than coastal regions. When one adds to the cost of desalination the cost of distribution, the comparison, already very unfavorable, becomes far worse. It may be that in a fairly short time we cannot afford to think about cost.

A second problem is concerned with the concentrated brine left from the extraction of fresh water from sea water. In a small scale operation one simply returns it to the sea and allows ocean currents to equalize things again. But when one begins to talk in terms of billions or trillions of gallons a year—figures comparable to our present total supply—this becomes an immense problem. Ecologists tell us that even a slight change in the saline content of the ocean along the coasts could have disastrous results to ocean life. Similarly some ecologists have worried about the by-product heat and, perhaps the knottiest problem of all, the disposal of radioactive waste materials. Any nuclear energy process now contemplated produces quantities of highly radioactive, toxic by-products. We shall consider these questions in the section on pollution.

Massive Redistribution

TWO SERIOUS PROPOSALS have been concerned with the possibility of taking water from the northern and northwestern parts of our continent, where there is at present an enormous amount essentially going to waste. The Ralph M. Parsons Company of Los Angeles has made a preliminary calculation of the costs of diverting some of this water to the western United States. In some thirty years, they believe, an investment of $100 billion would provide about 60 trillion gallons of water a year. They believe that the sale of water, at prices comparable to those now current, plus the sale of by-product electricity would make the project economically feasible. Another huge project suggested by a Canadian firm, T. W. Kierans, involves redistribution to the Great Lakes region of water now flowing wastefully to James Bay in Canada. If this project proved economical, as the Kierans firm suggests, it would provide another 3 trillion gallons of water a year.

Obviously these projects are enormous in scale and would take years to develop. Let's take the Parsons figures and assume about thirty years for completion of the huge installations. Sixty-three trillion gallons of water a year sounds most impressive until we note that it would add only 3 percent to our present rainfall supply in the United States. Of course, there is no reason whatsoever to believe that the taxpayers of Canada, Washington, and Oregon are going to sit still while we take away one of their most valuable natural resources, water. In very preliminary negotiations, in fact, the Canadian replies have ranged from a friendly but unshakable, "Hell, no" to distinctly malevolent comments of the "drop dead" variety. And we must always come back to the fact that our population is currently increasing at about *1.3 percent per year*. If it increases to 300 million, a figure often bruited about, by the year 2000 and if these additional people use water at the present rate, we shall need about 550 trillion gallons more water a year. In other words even these fantastically large projects would not come near maintaining our present position, far less "solving the water problem for the next 100 years" as enthusiasts have claimed.

Weather Modification

THE BEST WAY OF IMPROVING WATER DISTRIBUTION is by weather modification. If we could, at will, persuade water that now falls in surplus areas to fall in the dry Southwest, we could solve a number of present and future problems. By weather modification we could presumably bring to the land areas more of the fresh water that now falls uselessly back into the sea. If the weather could be manipulated so that rain fell gently and controllably, run-off could be reduced to the desirable minimum necessary to maintain the waterways. Crop yields could be improved greatly if farmers could count on rain as they needed it and good weather on demand. The benefits of weather control might even outweigh the controversies that would instantly accrue. There is, in fact, only a small fly in this ointment. The more we have learned about weather, the less prospect there seems to be of really controlling it in the predictable future. The experiments that seemed so promising a decade ago have proved of marginal importance.

The energy involved in even a smallish storm turns out to make nuclear weapons look like toys; no man-made force can be expected to make the smallest dent. What we need to learn is to control the distribution of solar heat and the release of the energy stored in clouds. It has been suggested, for example, that so simple an operation as dusting the Arctic with carbon would alter the reflectivity of ice and might change drastically the weather patterns of the Northern Hemisphere. I gather that calculations of the possible results are so frightening that no one has had the moxie to suggest trying it.

It is ironical to note that we have definitely succeeded in changing the weather inadvertently. Careful weather records reveal that polluted air has quite detectably changed patterns of precipitation over thousands of square miles of the United States and Europe. A series of peculiar rain and snow storms in east-central New York state was found to consist of quite significantly polluted water. The city of La Porte, Indiana, has recently (1951 to 1965) experienced levels of precipitation 31 percent higher than surrounding towns and much higher than formerly known in the area. There were 38 percent more thunderstorms and 246 more days with hail than in nearby communities. The city is about thirty miles downwind from the heavily industrialized area of Gary-South Chicago and careful analysis of the weather patterns shows that the variations in precipitation correlate directly with the ups and downs of steel production. This seems like the hard way of making rain, however.

Science News recently reported an intriguing hypothesis put forth by Lothar A. Joos, a climatologist with the Environmental Science Services Administration laboratory in Kansas City. He believes that irrigation has enhanced evaporation to the point of increasing rainfall 10 to 40 percent in the former dust bowl area of Texas-Oklahoma-Nebraska.

If we want to plan for the future and to try every avenue of possible hope in coping with the population of the world for the next few decades, few would seem to merit a gamble more than studies of weather control even though the possibilities of large-scale success seem, at the moment, very small.

4. / Water

SUMMARY

VARIOUS ESTIMATES have been made of our present water resources, of possible improvements in distribution of our current water supply, and of possible sources of additional water. Disregarding the expense and size of the installations being considered and the likelihood of such projects being undertaken, it seems quite clear that even the most heroic efforts can scarcely add more than a very few percent to our present water supply. Many urban areas—such as New York City—are right now teetering on the edge of serious trouble. It is clear that a very high proportion of the available water is already in use. Estimates of the population that we can support vary, but few experts believe we can continue at our present per capita consumption and at the present rate of population growth much beyond the year 2000. As usual, the question is one of how much we are willing to spend for water and how many compromises we are willing to make with our present standards of living. Also, as usual, the question is whether we *can* make the necessary adjustments rapidly enough to keep up with the increases in population.

5 /

Mineral Resources and Energy

"Now! Now!" cried the Queen. "Faster! Faster! ... It takes all the the running you can do to keep in the same place."

—LEWIS CARROLL

ONE OF THE CLASSICAL AREAS for Malthusian pointing with alarm concerns mineral resources. As everyone knows, the annual production of every mineral goes up and up as the per capita demand increases and the population doubles, but there has to be an end somewhere. On the other hand there has been no other area in which the predictions of alarmists have so consistently been disproved. I see no sign at present that lack of mineral resources portends disaster as convincingly as shortages of food and water and embarrassment of pollutants.

The point that can be made is that it is increasingly difficult to find rich mineral deposits of a size that is useful when measured against present-day needs. A good example concerns copper.

COPPER

ONE OF THE MOST SIGNIFICANT STRIDES in civilization was taken when man learned to use copper. Unusual in sometimes occurring free—rather than as an oxide or sulfide, for example— the metal could be found in certain places as pure crystals lying on the surface of the ground in quantities sufficient for primitive man. The crystals were highly malleable and could be beaten cold into tools and implements.

Skipping a few millennia, during which men, having run out of the pure natural metal, learned how to convert various ores into copper, how to purify it, and how to make it into such alloys as bronze and brass, we come to the beginning of the present century. By this time technology and demand had progressed to the point of processing ores containing about 5 percent copper or less. As Brown, Bonner, and Weir note, "Mushrooming per capita demand, rapid growth of population, and the spread of industrialization combined to make enormous inroads into the available supplies of ore. The grade of available ore dropped rapidly. By 1953 we were mining ores that averaged 0.8 percent, and even those containing as little copper as 0.6 percent were being processed."

At present we are using ever greater quantities of copper and are encountering ever greater costs of production. The price tripled in the thirty years between 1935 and 1965 while the United States' production doubled. Brown, Bonner, and Weir state that, "For every person in our country there [is] probably in existence [i.e. use] over 300 pounds of copper." A few years ago I saw a New York City subway display card claiming that the world's greatest deposit of high grade copper is now under the streets of the city in the form of electrical wires and cables. Could be.

We are confronted in the immediate future not only with a burgeoning world population, but with a fantastic rate of urbanization and industrialization in the underdeveloped countries. The thought of trying to supply 800 million Chinese or 500 million Indians with 300 pounds of copper each makes one quail. They would have to produce copper for forty-odd years at the *present total world rate*. But if both countries continue doubling in population in less than forty years they would then still be confronted with the identical problem if not a worse one! It becomes ridiculous. Yet there seems little doubt that these demands are going to be made and that they are going to be echoed from every part of the world. It is all too easy to agree with Malthus that the situation is impossible. But copper is quite widely distributed; the only real question is how hard we are willing to work and and how much to pay to get it. We isolated plutonium, after all, from uranium in which it occurred not at the five parts per thousand (0.5 percent) of copper in present low grade ores but at only a few parts per million. Needless to say, the cost was astronomical.

Other Metals

There seems little reason to consider the details of production, reserves, and demand for other metals. The situation is the same with nearly all of them, at least qualitatively. In the United States we have seen a tremendous increase in the amounts in use per capita. Steel leads by an enormous factor with the quantity in use per person increasing from about one ton in about 1880 to ten at present. Brown, Bonner, and Weir envision the possibility of an eventual 100 tons per person. In addition to the 300 pounds of copper, we find 200 of zinc and 100 of lead. The production of aluminum has risen something like ten-fold in the past twenty-five years. With all of these metals we find increasing dependence on importation of high grade ores as domestic supplies come more and more from the lower grades.

The questions of supply and demand of gold and silver are interesting. In 1930 the population of the United States was 123 million, in 1960, 180 million. Over the same time interval silver production dropped from forty-eight to thirty-one and gold production from 2.1 to 1.7 million fine ounces. Now this, of course, does not present an entirely fair picture since much of the gold and silver production is not consumed, only moved from one hole in the ground as ore to another as monetary reserves. But mining is falling behind—rapidly. When I first began lecturing on the subject of population problems I used to amuse myself by jarring the audience with the statement that the mining of precious metals was steadily falling behind the population and that money would soon go out of style. Little did I anticipate that within four years we would be making quarters out of substitute metals, that half-dollars would become scarce as hens' teeth, and that we would be minting no silver dollars at all.

And I note that economists are now muttering darkly that gold is outmoded—that the United States' paper dollar is far sounder. Well, at least you don't have to mine dollar bills and it doesn't take any more paper and ink to print a \$1000 than a \$1 bill.

Meanwhile silver has become more and more an industrial metal. By far its largest use is for photography, in which it is really consumed in the sense of being widely dispersed, as are lesser amounts in the electronics and brazing alloy industries. Jewelry is a major use and a considerable amount goes into dental work. The metal is becoming so scarce that the photographic industry is seriously looking for a substitute. For six years now, consumption of silver has outstripped production and the difference has been made up from monetary reserves.

The components of special steel alloys (nickel, molybdenum, manganese, and chromite) have always been scarce and expensive, but the demand has grown by leaps and bounds as have the prices. Tin production, since 1930, has increased only slightly; the price, as a result, has gone up nearly six-fold.

Despite all of this, the Malthusian fears that metals are exhaustible resources and would simply run out, have not been justified. The ratios of known resources to annual production indicate decades of continued availability at present levels for most key minerals and centuries for iron and aluminum. But we shall pay an increasingly stiff price for further population and burgeoning industrialization with its insatiable per capita demands.

NON-METALS

MANY NONMETALLIC MINERALS are vital to modern life. The average person never thinks of sulfur as anything particularly important because, unlike the metals, it does not appear as sulfur in consumer products. Yet sulfuric acid is vital to innumerable industries and the annual production is enormous. About 25 million tons were produced in 1965 as compared to 13 million in 1950. I mention this item out of a considerable group of nonmetallic minerals (for example, stone, sand, phosphate, cement, salt, gypsum) because we are seriously short right now. Demand has exceeded supply for five consecutive years and the problem is largely that the element has been too easy to mine from nearly depleted sources in the southern United States. There is plenty of sulfur, but it is—again—now increasingly to be obtained from secondary sources with much more work. A similar concern has been expressed with regard to phosphate—vitally needed in huge quantity to raise the world's food production. The rich sources seem limited; the price will rise. And so it goes.

ENERGY REQUIREMENTS

ALTHOUGH WE HAVE WORRIED PERIODICALLY about shortages of metals, it is probably in the area of energy-producing minerals that we shall experience the most difficulty. The basic problem is simple; except for nuclear power, the source of energy of the earth is the sun. Even though it is 93 million miles away, its contribution is huge. The data of Fig. 6 indicate a current usage in the United States of about 55×10^{15} BTU per year. In terms of the householder's unit of electrical power, this amounts to 1.6×10^{13} or 16,000,000,000,000 kilowatt hours per year. But the whole earth receives radiant energy at about 45,000 times this rate (7×10^{17} kilowatt hours per year). Using the commonly accepted figure of one horsepower per square yard as the solar energy input rate for the temperate-tropical region of the earth during sunny hours, one can calculate that a desert area roughly forty-five miles square receives enough energy to supply all of the present requirements of the United States. Our direct use of solar input is very limited, however. In fact no one has devised a technology that is reasonably inexpensive and efficient, though many authorities feel that we must expand our use of this enormous source in the near future to keep up with the sorts of demands projected in Fig. 6. Such ancient devices as the waterwheel and windmill depend on solar energy indirectly, as do the hydroelectric power plants we still use as a significant source of electricity. In the past century our major needs have been met increasingly through the use of fossil fuels—coal, oil, gasoline, and natural gas. All of these are indirect products of the photosynthesis in plants of bygone ages; all, in other words, represent stored solar energy.

The only nonsolar source of power available to us is nuclear. Starting from the development of the atomic bomb in World War II, we have begun to tap this source on an ever increasing scale, as shown in Fig. 6. Two major processes are possible. In the currently used *fission* process an element of high atomic weight (such as uranium, thorium, or plutonium) is caused to split into smaller elements with the release of huge amounts of energy. The bottom limit of this type of process is set by iron, which cannot usefully be split further. With elements below iron

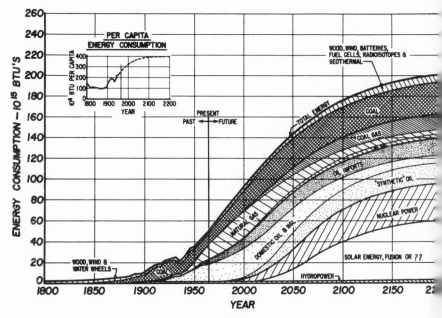

Note: 100×10^{15} BTU = 29,300 million megawatt hrs.

FIG. 6
ENERGY SOURCES IN THE UNITED STATES
(FROM L. P. GAUCHER)

it is possible to obtain energy by *fusion* of the nuclei. This is the main process that powers the stars; it is based on the fact that hydrogen at a high enough temperature and density will be converted to helium, the next heavier element, with the release of tremendous energy. Although this type of reaction has been used in the hydrogen bomb, it has not yet proved possible to contain the reacting materials at the temperature required—about 100 million degrees. At this temperature the elements form a

1 1 0

plasma, the fourth state of matter that in this case is too hot to be a solid, liquid, or gas. The plasma can be contained, it is believed, only by a magnetic field, since at these temperatures any possible material of construction would be vaporized instantly. Progress toward this goal has been very slow and expensive but continues.

Electricity is our main source of available energy and is useful because it is so easy and cheap to transport and is so adaptable to such a variety of purposes. Unfortunately electricity is not at all easy to store efficiently; the most practical storage (as chemical energy in a battery) is so far relatively inefficient, bulky, and expensive. Stored, portable energy is currently most cheaply and simply available in the form of carbon fuels and is released when they are chemically combined (burned) with atmospheric oxygen to form mainly carbon dioxide gas and water. As we all know, fossil fuel provides the motive power for virtually all kinds of vehicles. It is less appreciated that today it is by all odds our most important source of electrical generating capacity.

From our present viewpoint, the most important fact is the fantastic increase in energy demands in the developed countries and the ancillary fact that this is an increase in per capita use, as shown in the inset in Fig. 6, and thus represents a particularly vicious compounding of our population problem. Primitive man needed only 3000 calories a day for food. Fire-using, herd-tending man—depending increasingly on animal proteins, a secondary food source—raised his requirement to about 10,000 calories. In 1965 in the United States we used about 192,000 calories a day per person. This corresponds to a power consumption rate of about 12.5 horsepower or 9 kilowatts. It is worth noting that this is the equivalent of using for energy production the solar radiation-receiving capacity of about thirteen square feet of earth per person. If the projections of Figs. 6 and 7 are correct, we shall need four times this amount in the United States within the lifetime of the present generation of children.

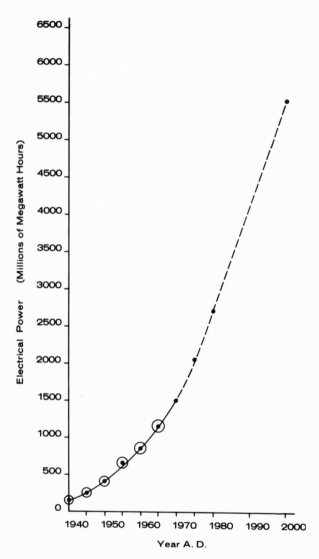

FIG. 7
ELECTRICAL POWER CONSUMPTION
IN THE UNITED STATES

5. / Mineral Resources and Energy

FOSSIL FUELS

THE DIREST PREDICTIONS HAVE BEEN MADE, from time to time, about impending shortages of natural gas, petroleum, and coal. We could easily devote pages to this subject. The use of these sources of energy now amounts—world-wide—to more than 2800 pounds per person per year or about 3.7 billion tons total coal equivalent. Brown, Bonner, and Weir have calculated that, "if all the people of the world were to expend energy at the per capita rate at which we expend it in the United States, the total rate of energy expenditure would increase approximately six-fold to the equivalent of that contained in 22 billion tons of coal each year." The estimates of geologists suggest that we have enough coal for 700 years at the *present rate of expenditure.* Even if we assume that industrialization brings the rest of the human population up to our rate of consumption, these resources would last over 100 years. Of course, if we continue to double the population as well as industrialize it, things will begin to grow complicated before then, though there seems little reason to think that we shall run out of coal before many other more disagreeable things happen. Petroleum and gas potential resources are believed to be capable of providing less than one-tenth the future energy of coal. Many writers have said that we shall begin to feel the pinch with petroleum by the end of this century. My impression, however, is that the geologists are continually extending our horizons with respect to fossil fuels. The incipient death of the petroleum industry has been predicted a wearisome number of times. But, beyond a shadow of doubt, petroleum, gas, and finally coal and shale oil will become more and more expensive to recover, and there *is* an end to the supply. Unlike the situation with most metals, we are really consuming the carbonaceous minerals.

There are two other aspects of this situation worth comment.

One is that from the point of view of an unfrocked organic chemist, it is a crime to burn fossil fuels. They constitute a virtually endless source of raw materials for plastics, medicines, dyes, human food supplements, insecticides, and a fantastic variety of other products. The other—that the burning of these forms of stored solar energy now contributes very considerably, if not principally, to the problems of air pollution—we shall consider in detail in the next section.

Nuclear Energy

The pollyannas find nuclear power a beautiful justification of the "God will provide" philosophy. Here we are, facing the ultimate consumption of what seemed originally like an endless supply of carbon fuels, and what do we have? Nuclear power, that's what. A pound of uranium—a piece no larger than a golf ball—can provide energy equivalent to that of a backyard-ful (about 1250 *tons*) of coal. This source of energy is now well established and is providing 'an increasing proportion of our power at prices that will more than compete with those of fossil-fuel electricity. As this prospect became a reality, there were those who commented grimly that we would run out of uranium before coal since it seems to be a rare mineral. But uranium is actually a plentiful element; it is *rich* uranium ores that are rare. As usual, we can supply the metal well into the future if at an increasing price.

The real energy bonanza lies in the use of fusion processes. These reactions provide the energy of the sun and other stars and require only water as a fuel. Water we have and you can't beat the price. We have not learned how to tap this source yet. The scientists who are working on the very difficult problem of containing a plasma at solar temperatures seem to be either optimistic or pessimistic depending more on their personalities than on real achievements toward this incredible goal. If the problems can be solved, however, the fusion process will provide energy beyond the dreams of avarice essentially for all time.

The importance of fusion can scarcely be overemphasized. But it has been. It is true that the power available will be essentially unlimited. But it will not, as even the informed layman seems to think, be free power. The capital investment in the installations will be enormous. Even with present comparatively simple fossil-fuel generators, the cost of the fuel is only about half of the price of the product electricity. As we develop nuclear power, economy and use will demand that the plants and the distribution facilities be enormously larger than those of today. Projections now indicate that even present-day type nuclear power will very soon cost less than fossil-fuel power—currently produced at about six-tenths of a cent per kilowatt hour in the United States. Eventual costs are now estimated at about two-tenths of a cent for fission-fueled plants on the assumption that a considerable part of the investment and other costs will be compensated by the sale of desalinated water at the plant for, perhaps, twenty to twenty-five cents per thousand gallons—a very high price by present-day standards. No one can make a reliable guess at the price of fusion power because we don't have the most remote idea of the kinds of installations that might be required. But even if the fuel is essentially free it seems doubtful that the final power cost will be substantially below the last estimate.

As we shall see, the intensive use of nuclear power raises very knotty problems of waste disposal and of dissipation of heat loads imposed on the estuaries or rivers used for cooling water. Fusion processes may eliminate or reduce the waste product problem, but by-product heat will remain with us and become even more of an issue as the size of the installations increases.

Nonetheless, unlimited power produced at a low cost from

our most plentiful resource—sea water—does promise to solve a host of other problems. Food production may be aided somewhat. It is tempting to think that plant cultivation might be expanded by widespread use of artificial light. The public has a virtually superstitious faith in the miracle of hydroponic farming and, after all, if we had twenty-four-hour-a-day light available. . . . All I can say is that ordinary plants have spent a long time getting used to things as they are, and I have not seen any statement by plant physiologists that artificial farming could work any prodigious improvements. On the contrary. Continuous algal growth might be feasible but one then talks again of unbelievably large installations. It does seem that production of semiartificial foods—if we are driven to these extremes—might benefit.

Almost every plan for future development of nuclear power is based on the assumption that the huge plants will be located at seaside, since only then will enough cheap water be available for cooling. Desalination of the sea water is counted on to provide a by-product that will reduce the power costs. As we have already commented, the amounts of water to be produced are appreciable so far as metered consumption is concerned, but the cost will be high even as a by-product. As a rule, moreover, the areas where water is most needed are far removed from the sea, for obvious reasons. The extent to which cheap power will facilitate the construction and lessen the costs of massive redistribution systems cannot be anticipated although one might guess that pumping water over mountains for long distances could become routine with unlimited cheap power. Capital investment would then presumably become the main cost factor. But it is a very large factor now.

The area in which an enormous expansion of electrical power might make a real change, it seems to me, is that of pollution. As we shall see, the largest and least controllable source of air pollution is the automobile. Domestic heating contributes another considerable increment that is difficult to eliminate because of the dispersion of the multitude of sources. It is obviously within the reach of present technology to replace carbon fuels completely for these purposes and, to a considerable extent if not entirely, for the industrial generation of steam and electrical power. But we should note that our *total* energy requirements (Fig. 6) are some thirteen times greater than our present output of electricity in the United States (Fig. 7). The burning of fossil fuels provides esssentially all of the nonelectrical and a large part of the electrical power. Even granting the possibility that capital costs will not allow reduction of the price of electrical energy to compete with steam from cheap coal, we shall increasingly find that coal is more valuable as a raw material than as a fuel, and air pollution enough of a problem to justify more expense if necessary.

It is not immediately obvious to me that nuclear power is going to help the problems of water pollution. Heat pollution, as we shall see, is an inevitable by-product. The question here is largely one of applying knowledge we already have, and the principal obstacle is cost and (decreasingly) public apathy. Indirectly a highly expanded economy fueled by nuclear fusion will contribute to the solution of innumerable problems, this among them.

We must not forget that the use of nuclear power carries with it the threat of *radioactive* pollution, but we are well aware of these potentialities and can prevent them from the beginning unless we allow the greed for power to override the manifest necessity for extreme caution.

SUMMARY

ALTHOUGH I CANNOT SEE ANY IMMEDIATE, nor even fairly long-term, reason for doom-saying with regard to mineral and energy resources, it is obvious that we are already paying and will continue to pay an ever heavier price as the population expands. Most minerals are increasingly hard to find in the huge, economically useful deposits needed for today's mass production mining. A few pounds of pure copper crystals once were a great find for an entire tribe of humans, providing tools and weapons probably for generations. Today, twenty-odd pounds of copper merely add one more to the 10 million vehicles we produce each year in the United States and scrap after a few years of use. As with the water problem, we see here again the compound exponential—human population doubling at an increasing rate and per capita demand rising steadily as a result of world-wide urbanization, industrialization, and demand for consumer goods. As a result, with some of the important metals we find supplies short of demands, with many we find an increased cost (even adjusted for inflation) as the good ores grow scarcer and consumption increases.

6 /

Pollution

Alas! Alas! Alas! Alas!

—A e s c h y l u s, *The Persians*

Introduction

"Pollution," unlike most dirty words, writes *itself* on our walls, and in doing so reminds us of the increasingly noxious quality of the very air we breathe. It is really amazing, in fact, that in such old, highly polluted cities as London, the inhabitants watched their buildings crumble for a century or more before it occcurred to them that the atmosphere might also be bad for people. That the water we need is tainted can be seen by simple observation of a large proportion of our rivers and streams. It is unfortunately true that we have taken completely for granted both our atmosphere and water. We have regarded them not only as limitless resources but, incredibly, simultaneously as bottomless cesspools. The human population has now reached the point at which we must question very seriously not only these assumptions but many practices based on them.

In our example of exponential bacterial growth and of the factors that might be expected to limit it, we included pollution—

the accumulation in the environment of the cells of by-products of metabolism. The growth of various kinds of microorganisms under certain conditions is indeed brought to a halt mainly by this blighting of their happy homes. The human race is even now in similar danger. Our concern with pollution has, however, grown enormously since I first became interested in these problems some eight years ago. The public has been made very much aware of certain risks that we are incurring and the United States Congress has even been persuaded to do something about it.

There is, of course, nothing new about pollutants. When your neighbor's dog reduces several square feet of your beautiful lawn to a wasteland in an effort to cover up things you would prefer that he did on his own lawn, he is merely obeying some antediluvian antipollutionary instinct—or at least trying to make it less apparent to his enemies (though today in a rather perfunctory way) that Kilroy was here. New, however, is *our worry* about pollution. Within the memory of most adults thick black smoke pouring from the chimneys of the local factory was the harbinger of prosperity and universally brought happy smiles. When the woolen mills in my home town dumped spent dye into the town river, no one paid any attention except fussbudgets like my mother who objected to my coming home from a little harmless swimming with my underpants a vague mauve or my entire person tastefully verdigrised. The fact that the town dumped raw sewage into the same stream did not really concern anyone. After all we knew that running water purifies itself in twenty-five feet. The sparrows in the street happily dined on horse droppings, God was in his Heaven and all was right with the world—or at least nothing was wrong that a little more smoke from the factory wouldn't cure. Would that we could have continued to dwell in that invincible ignorance. Unfortunately the populace has just about doubled itself since those halcyon days, industry has burgeoned enormously, and we have a few problems.

6. / Pollution

*Thank God men cannot as yet fly and lay waste
the sky as well as the earth.*

—Thoreau

Los Angeles' Classical Smog

CONCERN WITH AIR POLLUTION, in my memory at least,
began with Jack Benny's jokes about Los Angeles' smog.* The
"fogs" of London, and many other English industrial cities, were
traditional but had been a part of the environment seemingly
from time immemorial. That they had changed a bit in composition and virulence—as we shall see—was not immediately apparent. But Los Angeles had started out as a sort of foyer to Heaven.
One could awake in mid-winter to the coo of the mourning
doves, dress in streaming golden sunlight, enjoy breakfast under
the palms and, amid garden flowers, contemplate the snow on
the nearby San Gabriel mountains—pitying the poor unregenerate
schnooks back East who were shovelling the stuff. No more.
The mourning doves are drowned out by the complaints of the
taxpayers; the mountains have scarcely been seen for years; sunlight is a sometime thing that often filters vaguely through the
smog. Residents and visitors have grown accustomed to "those
days" when by 10 A.M. eyes smart and nasal passages clog. It even
seems wryly funny to stand around at cocktail parties surrounded
by tipplers with tears streaming down their faces. A considerable
number of species of flowers—for example petunias, snapdragons,
dahlias, and carnations—that formerly grew in profusion are
prominent in showing severe smog damage. More and more the
lush commercial farming that the area featured has been driven

Smog is a word coined by combining its elements of smoke and fog.

away from the city, partly by demands for suburban development but also because of smog damage to such crops as alfalfa, spinach, various kinds of lettuce and, it has been suggested, citrus fruit. The crop loss in California has been estimated at $100 million a year. And, as usual, one cannot help but wonder whether the obvious damage to plants, nylon stockings, and stone buildings is but the manifest indicator of concealed injury to animals, including humans.

A universal question, of course, is, "Why don't they do something about it?" The answer is worth consideration because it has implications for all of us. The fact is that the city has been acutely aware of its smog problem for about twenty-five years. In 1944, serious research was undertaken. Carefully made surveys to evaluate the contributions of various sources of smog were an early requisite, because at the outset everyone concerned was busy pointing his finger at the other guy. The industrialist pointed at home trash burning, the homeowner at the obvious plumes of evil looking smoke from oil refineries. Both screamed with anguish when the citrus growers lit their smudge pots to prevent frost damage. Autoists felt that diesel trucks were obviously smelling the place up something fierce; truck owners noted that there were vastly more autos than trucks.

Several years of difficult work were required to find the actual ingredients in smog that were damaging, to evaluate the contributions of various sources, and to understand the peculiar topographical and climatic conditions responsible for holding the smog in place. Legislation ensued, diligent enforcement followed. Unfortunately, however, the sad fact soon appeared that with other sources minimized, auto exhaust became by far the largest contributor to smog and increased at a rate that more than compensated for improvements in control of other pollutants. Huge amounts of money have been spent in efforts to find ways of reducing automobile exhaust or of reducing the amounts of its noxious components. The devices developed so far have been only partially effective and have been shown to lose efficacy rapidly unless maintained with considerable care. The total result so far? Little or no progress with the overall problem. The intensity may be somewhat less, but the affected area steadily increases and is now said to be 11,000 square miles.

It is not that heroic solutions have been neglected. The commission that studied the problem soberly considered not only the ideas of experts but every notion that every nut in Los Angeles suggested, and, as is well known, the smog density in the area is exceeded only by the density of nuts.

The problem is caused by a "temperature inversion." Normally air is cooler the greater the height above ground. But above Los Angeles, as above many subtropical areas, there is a sun-heated zone from about 1500 to about 3000 feet altitude in which the temperature *increases* with height. As currents of air and pollutants rise from the hot metropolis they cool and, when they hit the warmer air, tend to sink back instead of rising farther because cool air is more dense than warm air. To cure the problem, then, one must reduce the pollution, change the distribution of warm and cold air, or at least reduce the chemical reactions in the air that exacerbate its irritating character. Attention has been given to all three possibilities.

Having produced the pollution during the day, the irritated have tended to lie awake at night thinking of brilliant answers to the atmospheric problems. Among the notions considered and reported in *Science* by a former Los Angeles senior meteorologist, M. Neiberger, have been the following:
1. Elimination of the inversion. "All we have to do is heat the lower air hotter than the air in the inversion..." etc. "All we have to do is cool the air in the inversion layer . . ." etc. Long-suffering scientists have collected the data and done the calculations to show that either operation would require the

burning of 127 million tons of crude oil to produce the energy requisite to cause the change for a single day. Unfortunately, aside from the smoke produced in burning the oil, this meets the objection that it represents more than is produced in this oil-rich area in some twelve days. Heating the lower air, moreover, would give Los Angeles an average daily temperature of 100°F. As Neiberger has pointed out, residents who enjoy this temperature can solve their problems more easily by moving to the nearby desert.

2. Punching a hole in the inversion. "We could build a big smoke stack. . . ." The laws of physics show that the energy required to force the polluted air up a half-mile-high stack is exactly the same as the energy required in the first suggestion." But we also have to dispose of all that rubbish. "Why not use the heat from the controlled burning of the rubbish to 'burn' a hole in the inversion. . . ." Desirable as it is to get rid of rubbish, and massive as the installation would be, it turns out that the energy produced would "punch a hole" in only some one-quarter of one percent of the inversion-covered area and that the burning adds appreciably to the general problem. "We could lay huge smoke ducts up to the tops of the mountains. . . ." Calculation shows that it would be cheaper to lug the rubbish to the top of the mountains.

3. Blowing the smog away. "We might put great big fans on the tops of the mountains. . . ." In the first place air is hard to move. Lee Dubridge, President Nixon's science advisor and the former president of Cal Tech, has pointed out that the weight of air to be transported *each time* we wish to remove the pollution over Los Angeles is twice that of the total yearly production of steel in the United States, and steel can at least be loaded on freight cars. Furthermore, it can be calculated that to move the air would take one-sixth of the total electrical power output of the United States or twelve generating plants the size of Hoover Dam. "Put the fans in tunnels in the moun-

tains. . . ." Fifty tunnels each 100 feet in diameter with a fan capable of moving air at 100 miles an hour would move 0.2 percent of the air under the inversion. Blowing the smog vertically. "We could have big helicopters hovering . . . ," causes a number of meteorological complications, but even so would take something like 40,000 helicopters.

4. Using solar energy. The difficulty with all the previous notions is that the sun provides energy at something like a horsepower per square yard. The atmospheric situation reflects the action of this energy, whose amount, over an area the size of the Los Angeles basin (some 1500 square miles), is gargantuan (about 4 to 5 billion horsepower or kilowatts). Man-made efforts are utterly puny by comparison; the entire Tennessee Valley Authority power complex has a capacity of 18 *million* kilowatts. Almost any reasonable proposal must utilize the solar energy in helping us instead of causing trouble. "We could paint roofs alternately black and white to cause convection. . . ." Again the calculations have been made and indeed under optimum conditions the sun could be utilized to eliminate the smog by about 2:30 P.M. At this time there is little smog to eliminate since the afternoon sea breeze has usually done more than solar heating could. Reducing the sunlight to cut down the production of irritants might work, but the cure (an artificial nonirritant fog) would be worse than the disease even if it were scientifically and economically feasible. More complicated proposals involve, for example, saturating the air with water above the inversion to invert the inversion at night. But it would take five to ten times more water than is available in Los Angeles.

The whole point to this discussion is that a study of smog in Los Angeles over a period of decades, utilizing both the best scientific brains and the greatest nut-power of the United States, has led to only one conclusion: even though the atmosphere is as light as air, there is an awful lot of it to move away or clean up; pollution must be eliminated at its source. And the source is increasingly the human with his damned automobile. It is obvious that humans and automobiles are appearing much faster than solutions to the smog problem.

Effects on Humans: the Donora Smog

FOR SEVERAL YEARS, air pollution was good for a sure-fire boff anytime anyone at all had a chance to address a southern California audience. To many people, however, smog became more than a joke after the Donora, Pennsylvania disaster.

A heavily industrialized city of about 12,000 population, situated twenty-eight miles from Pittsburgh, Donora is located in a steep-sided valley and hemmed in on three sides. By the time of the occasion we are discussing (described in detail in a 1950 *New Yorker* article by Berton Roueché) the local steel and zinc plants had for years produced smoke and fumes that were at times annoying. Peculiar climatic conditions, beginning on Tuesday, October 26, 1948 led to the accumulation of a dense smog that proved intensely irritating to people with a tendency to bronchial trouble. Oddly, no serious complications ensued until Friday of that week, by which time it was impossible to see across the street in the daytime. Then, suddenly, in the early evening, all of the doctors in town began piling up phone calls from desperately ill people. Abdominal pains, splitting headaches, vomiting, and choking and gasping for air were the usual symptoms. As their phones rang continuously all night, the doctors found that they were hopelessly swamped; they could do little except try to keep the dying alive by injection of asthma supportives, such as adrenalin, and by administration of oxygen. Medical supplies of the whole area were mobilized; no one has any count of the people who were treated by the Red Cross, the police, the firemen, and other emergency groups.

6. / Pollution

The town's principal undertaker received his first call at 1:30 A.M. on Saturday and the second before he could leave his house. By the time he returned at 10 A.M., after getting badly lost in the fog in a familiar neighborhood, he had a total of nine deaths, and two other undertakers had one each. That day eighteen deaths occurred in a town that normally expected about one death per three days. More people who had collapsed died later, raising the total to twenty, or, according to some reports, twenty-two. Most were either elderly or perennial sufferers from asthma. No one knows how many were violently ill but kept going or were prostrated but recovered. The accepted estimate is that 6,000 people—one-half of the population—were seriously affected. At any rate, whether by coincidence or because the local mills shut down for the weekend, by Sunday the episode was over, even though the fog scarcely lifted at all until Sunday night. Despite intensive subsequent investigation by several groups, no single cause adequate to account for the severity of the symptoms was discovered, and the general opinion is that a combination of pollutants was responsible.

Although widely publicized, the toll from this smog was far less than the sixty dead from a similar event in the Meuse Valley of Belgium in 1930 and was only a bagatelle when compared to the 500-odd we kill on the highway nationally on a good holiday weekend. That we have come to expect. But the terrifying aspect of the smog deaths lay in the fact that this had happened in our beautiful United States, that no one had had any previous warnings, and that there was no assurance that similar or worse smogs were to be avoided in the future in Donora or elsewhere.

The Donora smog was a baby compared to the great London fog of 1952. By the time this yellow pall had lifted from the city, 4000 excess deaths had been recorded. Similar major incidents have now occurred in a number of large cities—Yokohama, New York, Sheffield, New Orleans, for example. Los Angelenos can take comfort from the fact that their city is now ranked fourth in a list of sixty-five American urban areas with air pollution problems.

Chronic Air Pollution

DEADLY EPISODES represent only the sudden unpredictable peaks of pollution that has come to be virtually accepted as a necessary evil in a multitude of industrialized cities. Many public health officials have tried to examine statistically the question of the average increment in illness and death due to regular year-in-year-out exposure to lower levels of pollution. As you might guess, many factors are involved and estimates vary. A committee appointed by the Medical Research Council of the United Kingdom has concentrated on bronchitis in England and Wales and found that in elderly and middle-aged men this affliction is forty times more common than among similar men in the United States and Scandinavia. They attributed 25,000 annual deaths to the syndrome and noted that the recent advance in antibiotic and chemotherapeutic treatment has produced no decline in deaths from this cause over some twenty-two years. A significantly greater incidence of recurrent chest illnesses was found in urban compared to rural communities. Among postmen the rates of absence from work attributable to respiratory disorders proved strikingly parallel to the indices of air pollution in the towns of their employment.

I cite this study only as typical of several that have been made with similar results. An ancillary aspect of the current furore in the United States over the effects of cigarette smoking has been the demonstration that a considerable incremental statistical hazard is presented to those in urban, industralized areas or perennially exposed through their work to industrially polluted air. Breathing the air of Manhattan is said to be the equivalent of smoking two packs of cigarettes a day.

6. / Pollution

National Air Pollution

IT IS EASY TO DISMISS THE EXAMPLES I have cited and other similar ones on the basis that they are isolated. . . . So we need to watch the levels of industrial air-wastes in a few large cities or places like Donora or Los Angeles with peculiar climatic problems. All we really need is a little breeze in any of these areas—a little good weather—and the problem is gone. . . . Would that it were so.

According to an article in *The Sciences*, we are annually adding to the air of the United States, through the burning of carbonaceous fuels, some 142 *million tons* of mixed gas and particulate matter. "In Manhattan alone, each square mile of the city is inundated by 60 tons of soot each month. Property damage alone, estimates the Federal government, costs citizens some 11 billion dollars a year, exclusive of the money lost because of declining real estate values in heavily polluted areas."

Although these incredible figures demand a solution, it has become obvious to all who have made studies and surveys that the chief villain is increasingly the least controllable source—the American automobile. Currently some 101 million motor vehicles adulterate the atmosphere annually with "86 million tons of carbon monoxide, sulfur oxides, nitrogen oxides, hydrocarbons, particulate matter, and the special chemicals, such as tetra-ethyl lead, added to gasoline to improve the quality of the ride." Where strenuous efforts and aroused public opinion have had effect, it has proved quite possible, though expensive, to reduce pollution from industrial sources, rubbish burning etc. to tolerable levels. The products of household and apartment furnaces are more difficult to manage because of their multiplicy and because the control apparatus is, so far, too complicated and expensive for small-scale use. But the fouling of our air by the automobile increases steadily with no practical control in sight.

Much brave talk in popular magazines about "blow-by controls" and "after burners" cannot conceal the fact that some fifteen years of increasingly diligent research have failed to provide a solution that promises to make any dent on the problem. Every year more automobiles travel farther and faster. It has been estimated that out of every ten gallons of gasoline purchased one escapes unburned while the other nine happily belch out of the exhaust pipe as products of combustion.

That GM and Ford are quite seriously investing considerable money in research toward an electric automobile (shades of poor dead Great Aunt Matilda with her vase of artificial flowers) is an indication that the handwriting of pollution is beginning to appear heavily on the Detroit wall and that they haven't found an eraser nor even a good whitewash. According to *Motor Trend* magazine some $18 million was spent on this research in 1967. The main difficulty is that we have virtually perfected the gasoline-driven juggernaut. It is going to take a pretty fantastic machine to compete, short of the point where pollution progresses from an occasional scandal to a major disaster.

An obvious question is how far the situation has progressed nationally. Manhattan air may be equivalent to two packs of cigarettes a day, but what about the rest of the country? Surely the vast majority of our citizens still breathe good clean air. Unfortunately, if one reads the daily papers and weekly news magazines with this question in mind, he becomes aware of a steadily growing list of complaints from coast to coast. The magnificent forests of Oregon are increasingly befouled with the sulfurous fumes of the paper mills. Even the pure air of Idaho (a state with only eight people per square mile) is falling victim to industrial and chemical waste. The roadside foliage of Vermont is gradually being shrivelled by automobile exhaust. The chemical industry is invading the great western deserts. Per capita demands for iron, paper, copper, power, chemicals all are increasing steadily, and it is indeed a rare section of the United States that one can fly over without seeing miles-long plumes of industrial aerial waste. Smouldering, stinking dumps are a feature common to virtually every hamlet and city.

World-wide Air Pollution

WITH NO TROUBLE AT ALL, I could continue a litany of the evils of air pollution, here, there, and elsewhere. But to me by far the most sinister fact of all is the tiny but measurable change in the world's air within a period of a few decades. Normally, carbon dioxide (at about 0.03 percent) is almost a trace chemical in our atmosphere even though it is the source of the main chemical component of all plant life. In the past few decades, however, the tremendous consumption of carbonaceous fuels has raised the carbon dioxide content of air by some 15 to 25 percent. The reason for concern at the presence in our atmosphere of this seemingly trivial amount of harmless gas is that it acts as a screen for outgoing infra-red radiation. The energy received from the sun reaches the earth's surface as a wide spectrum, but after interaction with plants, buildings, pavements, and the ground itself, a part of the energy is reirradiated from the earth as longer wavelength infra-red light. The well-known effect of cloudy nights being warmer than clear nights occurs because a cloud cover restricts this reirradiation from the earth. Similarly a greenhouse is warmed by the sun because the shorter wavelength incoming light is reemitted inside the greenhouse as longer wavelength heat energy to which the glass is impenetrable; thus it gets trapped inside and the house warms.

On a grand scale, then, as carbon dioxide accumulates in the atmosphere it tends to reduce the heat energy normally reemitted by the earth. This "greenhouse effect" should have raised the average global temperature 1.6°C. (nearly 3°F.) since 1900. You may consider three degrees as trivial, but even a small increase in the average global temperature is potentially of enormous effect. Gilbert N. Plass of Johns Hopkins University and Erling

Dorf of the University of Michigan have summarized much of the thinking in this area in articles published in *American Scientist,* a professional journal of the scientific honorary society Sigma Xi.

As we all know, at various times sheets of ice hundreds to thousands of feet thick have covered a large area of North America and Europe. Between these glacial periods the climate in much of the now temperate zone has been tropical. Examination of the fossil record for plants with well-known temperature requirements allows us to know with confidence the corresponding alternate colder and warmer average temperatures. The astonishing fact is that the difference between periods of glacial advance and subtropical climate is only about 5°C. (9°F.) At the moment we have in the United States an average temperature neatly halfway between the glacial and subtropical extremes. In other words, a drop or rise of about 3°C. in the long-term average temperature could throw our climate one way or the other.

One of the most widely held theories to explain these secular alternations of climate has to do with cyclic changes in the carbon dioxide content of the atmosphere. Plass makes a very plausible case for this theory. If its proponents are right—and we should understand that the theory is not universally accepted—we have already started the world toward a new era in which most of the United States would have subtropical weather. At present rates of the burning of carbonaceous fuels, we are increasing the carbon dioxide content of the world's atmosphere by 30 percent a century. Doubling it would be enough to produce the change we are discussing, and a return to carbon dioxide equilibrium by natural processes would take tens of thousands of years. The main question in a prediction of this sort is the rate of burning of carbon fuels in the future as the population doubles, redoubles, and rushes headlong toward industrialization. Presently known estimates of the reserves of coal and oil suggest as a limit that the burning of the total would add to the atmosphere *seventeen times* its present content of carbon dioxide. From 1950 to 1964 the number of motor vehicles registered rose in Europe from 12 to 51 million, in Africa from 1 to 3 million, in Asia from 1 to 8 million. We must ask ourselves such questions as what would happen if 800 million Chinese and/or 500 million Indians began to operate automobiles at a level comparable to that of the United States citizen of today. With 101 million vehicles, we have one per two people.

There is currently a great deal of talk about pollution-free gasoline, propane, electrical, or steam vehicles. We must keep firmly in mind that every one of these involves energy and that most of our energy comes from the burning of carbon fuels. To take the extreme—the electric automobile—we would simply swap local auto-produced pollution for industrial, power plant pollution produced elsewhere. Admittedly these sources are easier to control and admittedly we are going more and more from carbon-fueled power to nuclear power, but this change involves new and maybe even more serious pollution problems of a different kind, as we shall see.

There is, moreover, one slight catch to the idea that the increment of carbon dioxide we have added to the atmosphere is causing the global temperature to rise. The fact is that since 1940 it has really *dropped* about 0.3°C. Needless to say, any competent theoretician can work both sides of the street, and a recent notion is that although we are adding carbon dioxide at a spectacular rate, we are also adding dirt in the form of very fine dispersions. This, it is well known, would cause a *decrease* in the solar energy received and hence a drop in temperature. Thus we may temporarily have balancing effects.

The present picture is obscured by known short term and unpredictable zigs and zags of the global temperature caused by factors such as cyclic variations in the output of the sun and the presence in the air of volcanic dust. The important point, however, is that *the activities of man have changed the composition of the atmosphere of the earth quite detectably in only a few decades.* The long-term results are moot and the process is virtually irreversible.

Heat Pollution of the Air

AN INTERESTING POINT that I have scarcely seen mentioned until very recently concerns the undeniable fact that all of the heat produced by human enterprise must wind up somewhere. It is well known that the temperature within a city, for example, is several degrees higher than that of the surrounding countryside. The current annual world production of coal is 2.2 *billion* tons and of crude petroleum is 10.6 *billion* barrels. Whether this fuel is used to generate electricity, propel vehicles, pump water, or warm the baby's bottle is of no consequence. Eventually the result is the production of heat that can escape from the earth only by radiation. Kenneth Hickman has estimated that the heat being currently released into the atmosphere over North America is 0.2 percent of that received from the sun. This may seem trivial, but in addition to a rapidly doubling population we are confronted with energy demands per capita that are increasing by leaps and bounds. Expert opinion is strongly divided on future projections with estimates ranging from a 30- to a 256-fold increase in demands by the year 2010. General experience has been that projections in the past have been conservative, and no one can predict the results from the possible development of fusion power. If this gamble pays off we shall have available at minimum cost virtually unlimited energy which must eventually go somewhere.

The important point is that the earth is at equilibrium with the radiation received from the sun, but that we are adding quite appreciable and rapidly increasing amounts of energy from nuclear sources and releasing the stored solar energy of the ages through the burning of fossil fuels. What will happen if we continue to pour junk and heat into the air at an exponentially increasing rate is enigmatic. The situation is very complex. We can only hope that if we decide that we *are* damaging our total atmosphere we shall be able to stop in time.

WATER POLLUTION

In Köln, a town of monks and bones
And pavements fanged with murderous stones
And rags and hags and hideous wenches,
I counted two and seventy stenches!
All well-defined, and several stinks!
Ye Nymphs that reign o'er sewers and sinks
The river Rhine, it is well known,
Doth wash your city of Cologne;
But tell me, Nymphs, what power divine
Shall henceforth wash the river Rhine?
— COLERIDGE

IF THE PROBLEMS of air pollution are at the annoyance level, with occasional indications of serious results and potentialities, those of water pollution are somewhere between being a grade-A embarrassment and a catastrophe. With the air we are only alarmed because we always expected it to come to us in good shape, and its pollution is a new and still, let us hope, a relatively localized problem. We have, however, understood for decades that water, while purer than driven snow when it falls from the heavens, needs a little improvement by the time it flows past St. Louis. Hence even small towns are prepared to purify the water before we get it to drink. Unfortunately we must increasingly consider the degree to which water is now incorrigible.

Microbial Pollution

AS EVERYONE KNOWS who has progressed to his first health class in grade school, germs spread diseases, sewage contains germs, sewage has a way of getting back into run-off water. The happy notion that running water purifies itself is based (assuming that it ever had a basis) on the ideas that germs are harmless if diluted and that air and sunlight are anathema to them. Unfortunately none of these ideas is entirely correct and one can state without fear of contradiction that the Mississippi River would have to run a mighty long way (certainly hundreds of miles) from St. Louis before its water would become potable by natural processes.

Pollution of Rivers

I HAVE ALREADY POINTED OUT that we are running very short of water in many places and that about the only thing we can do is to make the available waters run around faster. As an extreme I have suggested one might argue that ideally the Missouri-Mississippi should arrive at the Gulf of Mexico as a trickle similar to that with which it begin its life in Montana and Minnesota. As rivers flow past us, we could conceivably use the water so many times that at the end unavoidable evaporation and transpiration would have consumed it all. We have noted that those who sail ships to New Orleans and barges to the upper reaches of the Mississippi, Missouri, Ohio, and into multitudinous tributaries, might find themselves opposed to this notion, as would the cotton farmers of the Mississippi delta. And there would be others. Also we are casting into these waters chemicals that we can rid ourselves of feasibly only by dilution in the sea (of which more later). We *cannot* use all of the river water. But obviously we want to use this run-off water as many times as we can and this means each user must find it possible to render the water again "pure." (I put "pure" in quotes because we now "purify" water largely by contaminating it—with chlorine, fluoride, water softeners, and other treatment chemicals. Better processes, involving distillation or microfiltration, are currently considered too expensive for large-scale operations.)

Human Waste

To GET DOWN TO CASES, we might consider a small assortment of specific rivers. In 1949 an interstate agency was formed to study the problems of the Ohio. Called ORSANCO (Ohio River Valley Water Sanitation Commission) it was, as usual, brought into being to rectify a situation already nearly beyond retrieval. The 1000-mile-long river has some 3.5 million people living along it in eight states. In 1948 less than 1 percent of these people treated the sewage that they dumped into the beautiful Ohio, yet the water of this river is used some 3.7 times on its way to confluence with the Mississippi.

The Connecticut River brings to my New England mind, at least, the picture of a beautiful stream wending its way peacefully through wooded hills and valleys. In a recent study, it was found that a sample from the river at Chicopee, in southwestern Massachusetts, contained 947,000 coliform organisms per 100 milliliters (about half a cup). Coliform organisms come, basically, from fecal material and are a standard measure of the contamination of water with sewage. The desirable coliform count for swimming water is less than fifty in this size sample; more than 1000 is considered awful. In other words the beautiful and historic Connecticut had nearly 20,000 times the desirable level of contamination for swimming. In another study it was found that Connecticut River water contained bacteria known to cause typhoid, paratyphoid, cholera, salmonellosis, tuberculosis, anthrax, and tetanus. Representative Jim Wright, in *The Coming Water Famine*, says that the water had in it "all known viruses"—a statement that

I would want to see documented. Let us say that it had a good round sample, including polio. Numerous intestinal parasites were found including tapeworms, hookworms, pinworms, roundworms, and blood flukes.

The Snake River, while flowing through the supposedly unspoiled Northwest, receives the sewage from some fifty cities and 150 industries before reaching the Columbia. A sample of the Cuyahoga River, feeding into Lake Erie at Cleveland, was found to have four times the bacterial count of average *raw sewage.* A once noble stream, the Potomac, flowing past our nation's capital, has been described as "an open sewer, comparable in its state of filth only to the Ganges." The Hudson is felt by some authorities to be hopelessly contaminated. The city of Utica dumps 15 million gallons a day of raw sewage into the Mohawk, an upstream tributary. Albany and Rochester each contribute 60 million gallons of sewage, New York City 450 million. Formerly teeming with fish, the river is now virtually devoid of them because the organic material dumped into the water uses up oxygen faster than it is replaced. Its main inhabitant is now a loathsome species of eel that lives on sewage.

It has been reported that only 1800 United States cities can boast complete sewage treatment, that 3000 are satisfied with partial treatment, and the remaining 27,000 simply discharge raw sewage.

Pollution problems are, of course, not confined to the United States. The majestic Rhine has bacterial counts, in places, of over 20,000,000 in a standard 100 milliliter sample. In Holland, where fishermen on the lower Rhine caught 100,000 salmon a year early in this century, the catch is now nearly zero and the fish taken are inedible. The Ganges and Brahmaputra rivers of India, and the Yellow River of China are scarcely more than open sewers. And so it goes, a list of heavily polluted major world rivers would include a large fraction of the total.

6. / Pollution

Plus Industrial Waste

THE FOREGOING, however, is just the briefest of resumés of one problem—sewage contamination. In addition come the sins of industry, also so numerous that they can be considered only by example. Seven paper mills in the relatively nonindustrialized state of Washington contributed a daily waste discharge equivalent to that from 8.4 million people—some three times the actual population of the state. According to Representative Wright, slaughter houses in Omaha, St. Joseph, and Kansas City discharge animal viscera, fats, hair, and other wastes into the Missouri in such quantities that the water literally runs red with blood in the vicinity and the huge lumps of floating foul mess have been mistaken for overturned canoes. The Raritan River in New Jersey became so polluted with industrial refuse that this so-called queen of rivers was, by 1930, one of the most contaminated in the country. Water sports, formerly a feature, had been discontinued and the stream had none of the fish and oysters for which it had been noted. A major program of sewage collection and treatment has now partially restored the river.

On Sunday, August 8, 1965, the Louisville *Courier Journal* devoted its entire magazine section to a study of the 425-mile-long Kentucky River. In page after page of colored pictures, this supposedly pastoral stream was shown from its origin, near the Virginia border, to its junction with the Ohio at Carrollton. The spring that gave rise to the first trickle of the North Fork had a rotting tire casing in it, and, because it was "tipped over" during adjacent highway construction, the water ran red from iron deposits. As a grim token of things to come, the first tree that the incipient river touched was dead. Only twenty yards from this spring, an outhouse hung over the bank of the rivulet. In the first 500 yards three sewer pipes emptied into it. A colored picture showed the North Fork two miles later, now a small creek, flowing through a tangled pile of rusting automobile parts, scrap building materials, and a broken discarded plastic laundry basket; trash that had accumulated behind a ramshackle outhouse whose corner conveniently overhung the stream. Raw sewage from the town of Hazard was shown—not untypically—gushing as a murky, bluish-grey sludge into the stream through a jumble of disintegrating tires, cans, and other rubbish. The water in one favorite swimming hole in this supposedly rustic setting was found to have a bacterial count between three and four times the acceptable limit—the bacteria being contributed by a nearby creek that had a count nearly forty times the safe value. At Hazard, the coliform count was "a terrifying 5200"—over 100 times the desirable level. The town of Whitesburg had a new water treatment plant, but did not use it because the river water it would have had to take in was too filthy. Whitesburg put its sewage through a treatment plant, but when the solids remaining from sewage treatment got to be a nuisance, instead of hauling the stuff away, the plant operators threw it over the fence into the river.

A characteristic kind of industrial waste plaguing the Kentucky is sulfuric acid, leached from the leavings of coal mining. Along with coal dust from the coal washers, it turns many of the Kentucky's tributaries into a black, lethal sludge. Residents who can remember fishing for catfish and bass now find no fish at all, not even crayfish. In many branches there is said to be no living thing—no water plants, no insects, no algae, no bacteria—because of the acidity of the water. Another source of trouble is the oil industry, which discharges waste into many of the tributaries of the river, coating the water with a black oily scum that fouls the rocks and banks. As the Kentucky nears the larger cities it becomes somewhat cleaner, and modern water and sewage treatment plants plus enforcement of laws against the dumping of industrial wastes restore the water, finally, to something like a healthy condition. The sewage from the state capital, Frankfort, adds a goodly slug of pollution with its entire sewage output, subjected only to "primary treatment." By the time it finally reaches the Ohio, the Kentucky has struggled down to a coliform count of 150—three times the desirable swimming level. This can, however, be regarded as a plus, since the Ohio at that point is rated as "grossly contaminated."

Disposal by Dilution. Of various chemicals and industrial by-products in run-off water, many, as slaughterhouse wastes, are easily removable or mainly disgusting; others, as acids from coal mining, are probably fairly rapidly destroyed by chemical re-action. Some, however, are only dispersed and undergo very slow destruction through microbial action or spontaneous pro-cesses such as oxidation. The limit to the reuse of run-off water is increasingly set by these noxious substances that are *not* re-moved by ordinary treatment and that must flow to the sea for ultimate disposal or dilution to insignificant levels. This problem, as we shall see below, has been stressed in a number of recent observations of the occurence in various situations of insecticides.

Pollution of Lakes

THE NEXT LOGICAL STEP in our pollutionary chain is the lake. Ponds and lakes are important not just as vacation and recre-ational assets—though it is the interference with these functions that usually first causes alarm—but as sources of water that we increasingly need. In theory lakes could support a considerable surrounding population indefinitely if the water were used, com-pletely purified, and reused, counting on new water only to replace that lost by evaporation and transpiration. Unfortunately we have assumed that they could also be used as perpetual dumps for human and industrial wastes. That this is an intolerable notion is clearly shown by the fact that we are currently most worried about our greatest and most seemingly limitless lakes.

The Great Lakes

THE GREAT LAKES are one of the largest bodies of fresh water in the world. They contain about 6×10^{15} (6,000,000,000,000,000) gallons of water or the equivalent of 3.3 years of total United States rainfall. Our previous figure of 5100 gallons per day per person total water requirement can be used to calculate that this supply would be enough for all the needs (including agricultural) of a surrounding population of 40 million people for nearly 100 years even with no replenishment and no return of used water. But the fact is that much of Lake Erie is so contaminated that it is unfit for use as a water supply; even when the water is chlorinated it is dangerous. The United States Public Health Service has recently issued a warning that ships are not to take water from Erie for cooking or drinking within five miles of the coast line nor within twenty miles of the large metropolitan areas. This injunction, however, is only the latest in a series of indications of what amounts to the incipient death of Lake Erie.

Fed by twenty grossly polluted streams, including the Cuyahoga River, which we have already used as a horrible example of pollution, it is claimed by some authorities that one-fourth of Lake Erie is now dead. The "death" of a lake describes a series of events that are referred to in the scientific literature as "eutrophication" —"eutrophic" being a term derived from the Greek and meaning rich in nutrient. The catch to this opulent sounding state of affairs is that these nutrients encourage the growth of algae. Decomposing algae consume the water's dissolved oxygen; fish need the oxygen. The fish and algae die, their stinking remains float onto the beaches. One kind of algae that is very common under these circumstances, *Cladophora*, has proved particularly clever. In both appearance and smell it is said to resemble nothing so much as masses of floating human feces. Soon both fish and tourists are gone. The fish data for Lake Erie are striking. Cisco, blue pike, and sauger were formerly taken from the lake at a rate of

45 million pounds per year. The catch in 1960 was 37,000 pounds, a 99.9 percent reduction, and it is now down to virtually zero (Fig. 8). Meanwhile the biological population of the lake has turned to a limited array of undesirable algae and fish, such as carp and alewives (Fig. 9). A large part of the lake is now reduced to an algal soup. The fish that are taken and the water from the

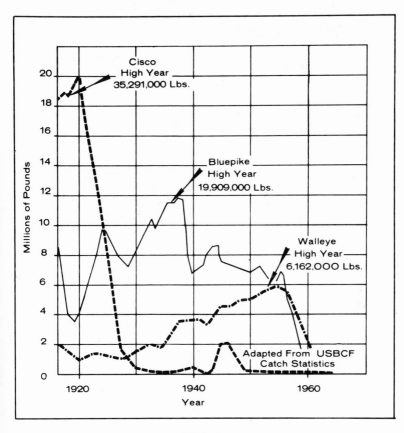

FIG. 8
DECLINE OF DESIRABLE FISH IN LAKE ERIE
(5 YEAR RUNNING AVERAGE)

143

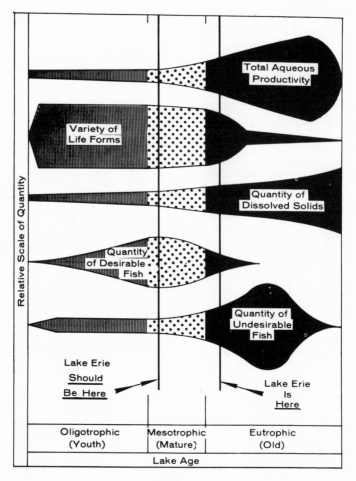

FIG. 9
Aging Indicators

lake even after purification are often so tainted as to be unusable for human consumption.

The causes of these changes are the pollutants, of course, and the picture is very complex. As pointed out in a recent article in *Science News,* "Every day 10 million people dump more than 18,000 tons of sewage, chemicals, fertilizers, and sediment into the lake." Human wastes create oxygen depletion; oils, tars, detergents, and other chemicals are toxic in many ways. Ducks, for example, have been killed by the tens of thousands because of surface contamination by oils and fats and from botulism, a disease induced by the growth of bacteria in oxygen deficient waters. The fish also often contain these bacteria. A few years ago there were several human deaths from eating improperly cooked Great Lakes fish. Phosphates, largely from detergents but also from agricultural fertilizer run-off, are being dumped into the lake at the rate of some 150,000 pounds a day. It is thought that algal growth depends mainly on phosphate, hence proper control of this pollutant is of prime importance. The algae also need nitrogen and carbon, but these are richly supplied in the form of huge amounts of human waste, fertilizer, and industrial products.

The smallest of the lakes, Erie is in the worst condition; on the other hand its problem are, for this reason, the most easily susceptible to attack. If the dumping of pollutants can be halted, it has been said that the normal turnover of water will bring the lake to an equilibrium state in something like twenty years. (Other estimates suggest that this figure may be optimistic.) A serious and very expensive effort is being made, but the sources of pollution are legion. Many conflicting areas of jurisdiction are involved in five states of the United States and in Canada. Even with the best of efforts and the resources of Federal tax support, an appreciable reduction—far less elimination—of pollution will take years. To lower the enormous contribution of the city of Cleveland, for example, will require not only the construction of much more elaborate sewage treatment plants but the separation of the waste and storm water sewage systems, since no one pretends that any city can afford to treat storm water in the way that it is necessary to treat human and industrial sewage. Although the Federal Government has moved vigorously into the Lake Erie problem, it seems that the various interests involved have not really progressed much beyond viewing with alarm and finger-pointing. Unfortunately the scientists have been called in late—as usual.

The "Lake Erie Report" of the United States Department of Interior Federal Water Pollution Administration offers a number of alternatives for the lake. To do nothing dooms Erie to rapid irreversible decline. All of the possibilities for rescue are expensive. As I read it, the costs of a good, perhaps, as the report says, "idealistic" program for Lake Erie would be $5 *billion* for immediate construction. By 1990 the total construction cost would be double that. In addition there would be high and increasing per capita operating costs. But even with this idealistic program, the most important point is that the report promises little more than a palliative. "It is uncertain that Lake Erie can be feasibly returned to its pre-existing state of aging, that condition which existed prior to man's appearance, or even to the condition which existed at the turn of the century."

In emphasizing the problems of Lake Erie, it must not be forgotten that the other Great Lakes are following the same pattern. Serious problems exists in southern Lake Michigan, as we shall see a little later, and the beginnings are visible even in Lake Superior. Although we have more time to handle these difficulties because of the size of these larger lakes, we shall have to pay the corresponding penalty of slower water turnover and much slower recovery once the pollutants are brought under control.

Finally, we must remember that the Great Lakes region, like the Boston to Charleston area on the Atlantic coast, is rapidly becoming a continuous megalopolis with an alarming rate of population growth and industrialization. Doubling of population is expected in fifty years. Like Alice and the Red Queen, we may have to run as hard as we can just to stay in the same place—undesirable though that place may be.

6. / Pollution

Smaller Lakes

THE GREAT LAKES are not the only lakes with problems. Increasingly rare, indeed, are those without problems. As people crowd around them, building permanent or summer homes, and as the tourist business increases—with much encouragement from Chambers of Commerce and Tourism Bureaus—the disposal of human wastes becomes an ever greater problem. Yet here one is dealing not with a few huge but controllable urban sources, not with hundreds nor thousands, but with millions of individual, often inadequate, dumps and septic systems. Even granting the establishment of legal standards (and this is usually fought tooth and nail) enforcement becomes a tremendous problem.

A prime example of one of the world's deepest, clearest, and most beautiful lakes now frequently said to be approaching ruin is Lake Tahoe, on the border between California and Nevada. Although conservationists have been in full cry for several years, claiming that algae are already accumulating, the limnologists (fresh water scientists) can see no serious, overall changes in the past ninety years. Who is right? Are emergency measures called for? Certainly the potentiality for damage exists, with an enormous tourist population, but if the public is willing to pay the price of careful management this almost unique American lake can probably be spared the fate of apparently similar alpine lakes that are patently undergoing eutrophication.

As the Cassandras keen with despair we can note that the problems of lake and stream pollution, caught soon enough, are usually solvable. We know what to do, we know how to do it. All it takes is time, determined effort, and willingness to pay the price. How soon is soon enough? An example of what can be done comes from the experience with Lake Washington at Seattle. In about 1950, an alert ecologist, W. T. Edmondson, saw early signs of eutrophication in this sizable lake (about eighteen miles long). Not only were typical pollution algae accumulating here and there in isolated locations (as in Tahoe), but the entire lake (unlike Tahoe) showed serious increases in levels of phospates and nitrates, the nutrients that make possible the excessive growth of algae. In Seattle responsible citizens listened to Edmondson, a committee was formed and headed by businessmen with drive and determination. The League of Women Voters (bless 'em all) got solidly behind the issue, and an all-out campaign was launched to save the lake. Because several communities were involved, special legislation at the state level was required to allow an overall bond issue. The total investment has now grown to $145 million. By 1963 a new unified sewage system began operation, linking all of the major communities surrounding the lake and discharging, apparently quite safely, into Puget Sound. This system was completed in 1968—*about eighteen years after Edmondson had noted the incipient eutrophication*—and already a very substantial improvement in turbidity (algal growth) and nutrient levels can be seen. Through prompt early action the lake has been saved.

But we must note the cost for this comparatively simple pollutionary problem of one fairly minor lake. If financing the bond issue will about double the initial cost—a not unreasonable assumption—we arrive at a total of about $290 million. This amounts to nearly four dollars per employed person in the whole United States or, since the Lake Washington area involves about one million people, of whom something less than one-half are presumably employed adults, a cost of about $600 per local wage earner. We might put this another way by noting that in essence every family in the area could have bought itself a full-sized, deluxe color television console for its contribution to the preservation of Lake Washington. In how many communities will we find a populace willing to pay this kind of price?

At an opposite extreme we may consider the lakes of Madison, Wisconsin. The University of Wisconsin, on Lake Mendota, has long been the envy of the academic world with swimming, boating, skating, and fishing literally at the doorstep of the class-room and laboratory. But this lake and several other nearby potentially beautiful small lakes have been classic examples of pollution and euthrophication. Scientists who have studied the Madison lakes for a full century have continually stressed the necessity for action. Despite numerous court cases, public campaigns, and changes in the methods of sewage disposal, the problems of repulsive algal growth and consequent hot weather stench persist. There is reason to believe that the processes of enrichment of nutrients have now progressed so far as to be irreversible. In essence, the lake sediments are loaded with nutrients for algal growth, the sediments of the shallow lakes are regularly stirred by natural processes, the algae grow, die, become sediment, and so it goes. Poisoning of the lakes with copper sulfate has provided temporary respite from the peaks of obnoxious algal blooms, but there seems to be no ready permanent solution. The residents of Madison heve spent a century dumping nutritious sewage into the lakes. If they want to improve the water the nutrients must now be removed, and no one has suggested a practical means. In several European lakes a similar, seemingly irreversible situation has been reported. Factors distinguishing such lakes from others where the process is reversible are very complex and not completely understood. Rates, duration, and specific kinds of contamination, shallowness of the lake, circulation of the water, and annual water replacement cycles all play roles. Even expert limnologists are sometimes unable to state definitely whether a given lake can be saved by presently known technology.

Today, in much of the developed world, we see an alarmed public. Even the innocent little lake in Vermont that I have visited for decades now has its pollution committee whose sole weapon is persuasion of vacationers convinced that it must be the other guy's sewage that is causing the problem. A sizable, man-made, Government-subsidized, flood-control lake here in Bloomington, Indiana,

149

has been open only for a year or two, but already the arguments, recriminations, and lawsuits occupy the newspapers regularly, with entrepreneurs seeking any and every way to avoid the insistence of the United States Government on adequate modern sewage disposal. The world now contains large numbers of lakes in far worse shape than Lake Washington. Will we always be willing or able to pay the high price of preserving beauty, recreation, a water supply, or a tourist asset? Or will we find an increasing number of lakes and ponds doomed by growing population and industrialization? Will increasing numbers of people live on the shores of a communal cesspool rather than pay increased taxes or watch the departure of industries faced with pollution restrictions? How often will we wait until it is too late and the situation becomes really hopeless, as seems to be the case in Madison? Who will invest the money and time to do the research needed to provide a basis for decision and optimum action for our thousands of lakes? Where will we even find the required scientists? The only sure conclusion is that the problems of our lakes are not going to solve themselves.

Pollution of Bays, Estuaries, and Coastal Waters

It is grimly entertaining to speculate how long it will be before politically compelling evidence is obtained to cast doubt on our fatuous belief that we can dump anything in any quantity into our run-off water because it will wind up in the "limitless" ocean. We shall shortly see reasons to question our assumption that the oceans are of infinite size. But the main problem in the ocean for some time will be that of mixing and distribution; although there is a lot of water for dilution in the ocean, trash tends to linger distressingly in the tidal region.

The principal indicators of pollution damage along our coasts have been shellfish. Chesapeake Bay produced 10 to 12 million bushels of oysters a year in 1908. By 1940 this was reduced to

4.5 million and the yield now stands at about 1 million bushels. Raritan Bay was famous for its oysters, now it produces none. Great South Bay on Long Island produced 350,000 bushels in 1937, now zero. The state of Maryland was noted as the world's leading source of oysters, now it is far down the list. In Alabama the loss of oysters to pollution is estimated at $22 million worth per year. A massive attempt to improve the oyster industry in Great Britain has failed and the culprit is clearly pollution. Clams were a New England delicacy, sold fried in boxes like popcorn when I was a boy. Maybe still, but now yearly the clam is harder to find. In Connecticut the beds have moved more than seven miles downstream from the former sites as pollution of the Connecticut River has increased. Pollution not only kills clams, it makes the survivors unfit for human consumption. Several known epidemics of hepatitis have been traced to polluted clams, and beds are being condemned. In Massachusetts 15,000 acres have been so lost, in Maine 75,000, in Chesapeake Bay, where the rate of loss is about 500 acres a year, 20,000. Shrimp have proved to be particularly able concentrators of DDT, lobster crops are declining alarmingly and no one knows the cause, though pollution (in addition to claimed over-fishing by the sinister Russian trawlers) is a likely suspect. Adequate study of bays and estuaries is just beginning, but the ecologists are already uncovering all sorts of repulsive facts about the influence of industrial wastes, particularly insecticides, on the whole population from plankton to water fowl and edible fish.

Despite such constant indications of our mistreatment of our coastal areas, by and large we continue dumping. Whole beaches in southern California have been closed because of sanitary pollution, but the public seems to regard it as an act of God or a bit of bad luck—like catching a cold. When I was living in Berkeley, an article appeared in the local papers to the effect that at a national meeting of sanitation engineers, San Francisco Bay had been described as "the world's biggest cesspool." My impression is that other areas could give it a lot of competition for this dubious honor, but the appalling fact is that no one much seemed to care. Unlike ponds and lakes, bays and estuaries apparently are regarded as belonging to no one. They are just there—a part of the limbo that is the world's seas. We are about to see a new and potentially very serious challenge to this attitude with the advent of nuclear power and thermal pollution on a really huge scale.

I promised at the outset to look at both sides of various questions. We must note, under this rubric, that not all is black. It is even possible that we can put thermal pollution to work for us, as we shall see, and there has already been a change in our pollutionary habits that is at least aesthetically on the positive side. Only a few years ago one could virtually walk dry-shod across lower New York Bay, supported by the floating condoms. With the advent of the pill, the bay and beaches are again safe for the innocent—the only catch being that there are no longer any innocent of breeding age.

Petroleum Leakage

A NEW and most repulsive aspect of pollution has to do with the effects of petroleum and petroleum products on coastal waters. For years there has been periodic difficulty, here and there, with tanker ships from which residual crude oil or other petroleum products have been pumped into the Great Lakes or bays or harbors. In a number of places laws have been passed forbidding such action. They have frequently proved difficult to enforce because ship crews pump out ballast or flush out tanks, reload, and disappear before anyone knows what has happened.

An entirely new problem appeared with the advent of enormous tankers with capacities of more than a *hundred thousand tons* of petroleum. Inspired partly by the closing of the Suez Canal, partly by the ever higher costs of labor in the merchant marine, these tankers are taking over from the 16,000 ton ships of the World War II period as fast as they can be built, and the size gets greater each year. The latest to come from the Japanese shipyards have capacities of over 200,000 tons and current talk is of supertankers in the half-million ton range.

Then, on March 18, 1967, the *Torrey Canyon,* a tanker of 117,000 ton capacity, ran aground near the southwest tip of England. The crude Kuwait oil began to flow toward some of England's most famous beaches. Sea birds in the tens of thousands became oil coated; it proved largely impossible to save them even when they were caught and cleaned. Of 8000 treated, only about 1 percent were believed to have been rescued. Amid predictions that the beaches might be ruined forever, all sorts of measures were tried. The oil would not burn, and the use of 10,000 tons (2 million gallons) of detergents on the Cornish beaches proved a cure far worse than the disease. Very heavy killings of phytoplankton, zooplankton, and intertidal animals resulted with a large part of the eventual damage traceable to detergents. Apparently the best solution so far is the quite simple-minded one of soaking up the oil with straw. As one expert put it at a conference called by the United States Government in 1969, "In an age when we can reach the moon, we should be able to do better than this." I have a suspicion that we are going to be pretty sick of this phrase before we are through, but one can scarcely deny its applicability in this instance. *Time* magazine noted, "In the past five years, 94 tankers have foundered; two collisions occur every week." The 207,000 ton *Marpessa* exploded and sank off Africa late in 1969, but fortunately was empty at the time. A number of other similar, less destructive episodes have occurred.

Of an altogether different order of magnitude, however, is the new menace of leaking off-shore oil wells. The incident in the Santa Barbara, California, channel in 1969 has been followed by several others, and enormous immediate damage to beaches, birds, private boats, fishing, and local sea life has occurred (though not justifying the most extreme of the predictions). As this section is being written, another instance of potential major importance is occurring as the result of leakage from an out-of-control oil well off the coast of Louisiana. It is all very well to claim that the petroleum company is at fault and that damages must be paid, but how does one assess the upsetting of the whole marine ecology of a huge area? In the episodes that have been investigated, certain types of marine life have been virtually wiped out, including valuable food fish and shellfish. Will this resource recover? In how long? Biologists are studying the damage, but the problems are complex and it may be years before we know the answers.

Needless to say much attention is being devoted to preventing future leaks and to curing those that do occur. A presidential panel has estimated, however, that with the great increase in off-shore oil drilling we face at least one such episode a year after 1980.

Destructive as these oil leaks have been, I cannot really get terribly excited about them in comparison to other pollutionary problems. I am sure I would feel quite different if I owned Santa Barbara beach property or depended on fishing for a living, but off-shore leaks are a local phenomenon, the oil industry is squarely to be blamed, legislation will surely provide penalties stiff enough to ensure development of preventives and cures. I personally suspect that the worst pollutionary problems that we face are not, by and large, those involving big industries, callous and indifferent though they have often been, but those involving multitudinous smaller businesses scattered all over the country and even more the tens or hundreds of millions of individuals each contributing his bit from a source that is not easily controllable, as the automobile or home trash burner or furnace or septic system.

The net conclusion on pollution of bays, estuaries, and coastal waters is that the problem is not only one for the small minority who try to make a living from tourists or shellfishing, but for all of us. We have changed, are changing, and have the potential for changing very appreciably the coastal environment. Even if we totally neglect the scenic and recreational values of the sea coast, we must remember that we are talking of depending heavily on the future food production of these waters. We tend to forget that although we in the United States regard sea food as rather a luxury, in much of the world fish are even now a major source of food. We have seen that there are arguments about the potentialities of the sea for future food production, but as we shall see, we cannot talk about huge increases of food from the sea on the one hand and using the oceans as cesspools on the other.

Ultimate Disposal

WITH A CONSIDERABLE PART OF OUR WASTES, we adopt the attitude that we need only dilute them enough or remove them from our attention by a sufficient distance. Ultimately we depend on the world's oceans to accomplish these purposes. There are three classes of pollution that will claim increasing attention in this regard.

Pesticides

THE MOST EFFECTIVE OF THE PRESENT supposedly selective "second-generation" insecticides are also toxic to higher animals, as was emphasized quite sufficiently, not to say grossly overemphasized, in *Silent Spring*. The late Rachel Carson to the contrary notwithstanding, no reasonable person can doubt that we are irretrievably committed to the use—but hopefully not the continued abuse—of pesticides. As pointed out in a spate of post-*Silent Spring* articles by industrial apologists and also by presumably disinterested scientists, pesticides have saved hundreds of thousands of lives for every one lost by accident or gross misuse. Of 152 deaths, of which ninety-four were of children, attributable to pesticides in the United States in 1961, for example, 104 came from "first-generation" pesticides (that is general poisons such as arsenicals). Not a single death in that or any subsequent year is attributable to the eating of food contaminated with insecticide by agricultural spraying. As a comparison we might note that the death rate from the automobile is now well over 50,000 per year and that accidents with firearms kill more than 2000 people annually. Aspirin, one of our most harmless medicines, kills over 100 children a year through accidental misuse.

Thomas H. Jukes, in an article in *American Scientist*, lists thirty diseases that are now controlled or controllable by the use of DDT. These include such world-wide killers as malaria, filariasis, plague, yellow fever, typhus, and yaws, to name only a few of the most important. Paradoxically, insofar as the population problem is concerned, DDT has been a major factor in the increase of life expectancy in many areas. Jukes points out that, "the population of Madagascar, which had been stationary for many years, doubled between 1947 and 1959 following the initiation of an anti-malaria campaign in 1949. . . . Malaria in India [was] reduced from 75 million cases to less than 5 million and the average expectancy of life in India rose to 47 years as compared with 32 years before the eradication campaign. Knipling in 1953 estimated that at least 5 million lives had been saved and 100 million illnesses prevented through the use of DDT. The Pontine Marshes, for 2,000 years an uninhabitable morass of malaria, now [are] inhabited by 100,000 healthy people. The use of DDT is considered to have prevented a devastating typhus epidemic from sweeping through Europe [in 1945]."

In considering the food problem, of course, we must take into account the increases in agricultural production due to the use of pesticides. Because of the variety of factors involved in improved agricultural yields, accurate figures are difficult to obtain. Nonetheless there are numerous examples of dramatic improvements attributable almost entirely to modern pest control. Ralph L. Metcalf reported to a meeting on "Research in Pesticides" in 1964 that insects are even now estimated to destroy over 10 percent of potential crops. In the first two years after the introduction of DDT, the yield of potatoes increased 56 percent per acre in New York state and 68 percent in Wisconsin. Sweet corn in the Coachella Valley of California was over 99 percent wormy before the use of this insecticide, far less than 1 percent wormy afterwards. The Imperial Valley of California now provides cotton in yields nearly four times the average of the rest of the United States, yet cotton production was abandoned in this area forty years ago as impossible because of insect damage. Control of nematodes has raised yields of lemons 22 percent, oranges 33 percent. Production of wheat in New Zealand has improved up to 54 percent as the result of modern pesticides. These are only the briefest samplings of many examples.

The advantages are so compelling to all experts that we are now using insecticides in enormous quantity. Over 45,000 pesticide formulations are registered with the United States Department of Agriculture, and annual production totals about 800 million pounds. But the picture is not one of unalloyed benefit. Despite the protestations of the special pleaders, it is a fact that these poisons are adding unbelievably to the problems of pollution world-wide. A large proportion of the pesticide applied to a crop either remains in the ground or washes away and winds up in our rivers. In a considerable number of well-publicized episodes, contaminated river water has killed fish by the millions. A particularly notorious series of incidents involved insecticides in the lower Mississippi. Studies by several research teams revealed that about 3.5 million fish were killed in 1960, a million each in 1961 and 1962, and 5 to 10 million in 1963. Endrin, used on cotton and sugar cane, and endrin wastes from a chemical plant near Memphis seem to have been the principal causes.

The pesticide industry has been active in describing the levels in average river and coastal waters as far below human toxicity and the levels in the seas as totally negligible. Unfortunately a few disturbing facts have surfaced. It is true that the concentrations in the coastal waters and seas are very low, but it is also a fact that many marine organisms have shown a distressing ability to concentrate some insecticides. DDT, for the production of which I must take a certain personal responsibility, has been widely studied because it seems to be nearly indestructible, has been in widespread use for some two decades, and is particularly easy to detect in extremely low concentrations. As described in an article by George M. Woodwell, in *Scientific American*, about half of the four pounds per acre applied to a New Brunswick forest to control spruce budworm was present several years later in the forest soil. A marsh that had been sprayed for mosquitos over a period of twenty years was shown to have up to thirty-two pounds per acre in its mud. The plankton in this marsh contained some 0.04 parts per million of DDT while the minnows that fed on the plankton had concentrated it in their tissues to twenty-five times this level. The gulls that fed on the fish had further concentrated the insecticide to seventy-five parts per million (a total increase of some 1900-fold) and carnivorous animals in the vicinity had concentrated the DDT about 1000-fold. It is clear, according to Woodwell, that the next level in the food chain would involve animals either killed outright by the insecticide or seriously injured in their ability to reproduce. DDT is now a virtually ubiquitous component of animal life. New born human babies have been shown to contain detectable quantities; the chemical has been demonstrated in Antarctic ice and penguins. Two species of free-swimming Atlantic Ocean seals were found to contain appreciable amounts of DDT.

6. / Pollution

In an article in *Science* in 1963, studies were reported that showed pink shrimp to be poisoned by the presence in the water of less than one part per *billion* (0.000,000,1 percent) of heptachlor. The growth of young oysters was inhibited by only three parts per hundred million of three common insecticides and by one part per 10 million of several others. In the years 1954 and 1956 the salmon population of the Miramichi River in New Brunswick was virtually wiped out by the use upstream, to control spruce budworm, of but one-half pound per acre of DDT. The death of the salmon occurred indirectly, the insecticide killing the stream insects on which they normally fed. In British Columbia the coho salmon crop of four different streams was nearly 100 percent destroyed by the use of DDT at one pound per acre. Coho salmon was introduced into Lake Michigan to control the useless alewives that had replaced the food fish in the increasingly polluted lake. At first the coho was a great success. But unfortunately he is at the end of a considerable food ladder and now turns out to contain so much DDT that the FDA has declared the coho unfit as human food and has banned interstate shipment of it.

These examples are only a very few of many that could be cited to show the lethal effects of insecticides in food chains so complex that the species killed may be far removed in both space and time from the site of application. That the problem of concentration of pesticides even in the "limitless oceans" is neither local nor merely theoretical is indicated by observations reported in *Science* in March 1968. The report also underscores a point (very frequently made in bird studies) that besides killing outright, insecticides may have other long-term effects on an entire species. The already rare Bermuda petrel currently shows a decrease in reproductive rate of 3.25 percent per year and with continuance of this trend will be extinct in 1978. Perhaps you could not care less about the fate of the Bermuda petrel, since the bird is hovering on the brink of extinction anyway. The gross

159

exaggerations and sentimentality of *Silent Spring* have rather disarmed the scientist who sees such a bird not as our feathered friend but as an indicator of pollutionary problems. For the distressing part of the *Science* report lies in two facts known only to the specialist. 1) This bird is completely pelagic—that is to say it feeds and lives entirely in the open sea and visits land only rarely to breed. 2) The decline in birth rate is known almost surely to be due to insecticides, presumably DDT. Not only the bird but its eggs and chicks show amounts of DDT known from other studies to be clearly of significance in the declining reproduction of carnivorous species. Similar relationships between declines in reproduction and insecticides have been implicated in populations of ospreys, woodcocks, falcons, eagles, herring gulls, and quail. With the other species it is possible to regard the problem as unfortunate but strictly localized; the Bermuda petrel, however, is accumulating the insecticide by feeding on cephalopods (such animals as squids and cuttlefish) *in the open sea*. This is the first indication that I have seen that we can no longer consider even the world's oceans as an infinitely large cesspool. Obviously we must begin to examine with some care our long-cherished assumption that the streams and oceans can carry away and render harmless unlimited quantities of any unwanted material.

A realistic evaluation of the present and future insecticide situation is impossible because we are only beginning to gather the necessary information. Ecologists, who study the total interrelationships of organisms and their environment, have learned just enough to be alarmed at the complexity of many such biological systems and the inadequacy of our information. An ancient ecological joke relates the strength of the British Empire to the number of old maids. It runs something like this:

Old maids keep cats; the more old maids the more cats. The more cats, the less mice. Since skunks prey on mice, therefore the less skunks. But skunks also destory bees' nests, therefore the more bees. More bees means better pollination of animal fodder, and thus more beef. And clearly the more meat, the more virile and vigorous the army and navy and hence the stronger the Empire.

One could, of course, complete the cycle by noting that the more virile and vigorous the military, the fewer old maids. This topic is surely fodder for several Ph.D. theses if not historical treatises. The ecologist, however, has encountered numerous real and far more complex situations in which spraying insecticides or herbicides for altogether worthy objectives has instituted chains of events with repulsive and often far-removed consequences. And it *has* happened, as in the coho salmon instance, that the human has been a possible eventual victim, protected—one hopes—by the diligence of those who watch over our foods.

It should be strongly emphasized that today no technically informed people are advocating abolition of insecticides. It is agreed that what is needed are more selective insecticides and more sensible application in place of today's gross, shotgun, by-the-calendar, overkill. It may be that we shall have to accept some bird or fish killing as the price of optimum food production. The important thing, it seems to me, is to be aware of what we are doing and to know consciously that we are paying a price, but that the long-term result is bearable—the price acceptable.

In the establishment of fundamental principles, it all too often seems to the outsider that the biologist or ecologist deals with trivial and remote problems. Ecologists, particularly, have a distinct knack for sounding as though their worry was not for the human but solely for some relatively obscure or seemingly useless species of animal. They seem involved in an unending fight for lost causes—for the preservation of some creature that has apparently played out his evolutionary role even without the *coup de grace* delivered by the human with his destruction of a habitat or pollution by insecticides. But the human *is* upsetting the balance of natural populations all over the world in multitudinous ways. Only the most dramatic of these ordinarily come to our attention. Only rarely, as with the blue whale, is it obvious that we are short-sightedly destroying a valuable asset. Even if one has no concern whatsoever for other creatures, no feeling that we have a responsibility to other forms of life, it is still true that the fate of a bird may be a strong indication of trouble in store for *us*. If accumulations of DDT are preventing the breeding of birds, could the same fate overtake the human? There are scientists who are genuinely worried. If radioactive wastes from power production or nuclear weapons are damaging forever the genetic material of an unimportant fish, could the next step be the human? There are those who think so. It is obvious that no one expected that DDT would turn out to be essentially indestructible, cumulative, and very damaging to higher animals. It took us over a quarter-century to find out that DDT is a menace. Now we know that it is. We are beginning to ban its use. Splendid. What other little surprises of our own making are lying around unobserved because they are even more insidious?

Radio Isotopes

Into my heart an air that kills
From yon far country blows.
        —Housman

THIS BRINGS US TO ANOTHER CLASS of pollutant with peculiar properties—the radio isotope. Unlike all other dangerous pollutants these cannot be rendered harmless except by the passage of time. They must be disposed of either by segregation until the requisite time has passed or by dilution to a point of no danger. Both methods are being used. But dangerous potentialities exist even supposing that we somehow manage to avoid committing racial suicide by major nuclear warfare.

Disposal by dilution has been studied most with respect to radioactive isotopes released into the air by bomb testing. Although one is inclined to believe that anything loosed into the atmosphere is just sort of wafted away into the gulf of endless space, observations have shown that what goes up comes down again, sooner or later, and that it tends to come down in dollops instead of being smoothly diluted to harmlessness. Even worse, radio isotopes of certain kinds tend, like pesticides, to become concentrated as they move through the food chain. Cesium 137 is a particularly obnoxious example. As fallout from bomb testing, it came to the ground in Alaska with the gentle rain. Lichens soaked it up, caribou ate the lichens, Eskimos ate the caribou. At each step a concentration of about two- to three-fold could be demonstrated, with the result that many Eskimos are now daintily radioactive. It was largely on the basis of these findings that scientists forced abandonment of plans for a large-scale attempt to use nuclear explosions for blasting a harbor in Alaska.

Nuclear reactors and nuclear power plants produce radioactive material that must be disposed of. Depending on its design, a reactor may release appreciable radioactivity into the air and into the water used to cool the reactor. With proper management neither of these is believed a source of potential danger. We should point out, however, that there is very serious scientific debate on this score. As eminent and sensible a scientist as the late H. J. Muller (Nobel Laureate in 1946) devoted a large part of his attention to the argument that *any* increase in the background radioactivity causes *some* genetic damage and that *any* genetic damage is intolerable. Many geneticists would agree with him, but as in a great many situations we find ourselves compromising the ideal with the practical, the seemingly necessary, or the expedient.

Quite a different matter is the radioactivity of spent nuclear fuel. A hideous mixture of dozens of isotopes, this material is not only fiercely radioactive, but potentially dangerous by anyone's estimate for hundreds of years. Dilution, even in the deep ocean, is considered quite impossible because we simply cannot be sure that ocean currents will not release it into regions where it can enter a food web with totally unpredictable results. The solutions to this problem are either to embed the spent fuel in concrete in oil drums to be dumped in deep water, to bury it in a very carefully selected place where no conceivable accident (earthquake, flood, seepage, etc.) can return it to biological circulation, or to store it in huge tanks. All of these solutions are very expensive. And there is always that nagging doubt—is it really absolutely so that the drums will not rust, the concrete disintegrate . . . ?

So far the problems have been difficult and expensive of solution but at least possible to handle.

In one year some 180,000 cubic feet of waste were buried by the Oak Ridge plant operators, 70,000 in Los Alamos, 60,000 at the National Reactor Testing Station and similar amounts at Hanford and Savannah River. From 1946 to 1960 21,000 oil drums were dumped into the Pacific and over 23,000 in the Atlantic. But these examples of waste disposal come from the infancy of the Atomic Age. The gross nuclear power output in the United States alone has risen nearly ten-fold in five years—from 590,000 megawatt hours (a megawatt is a million watts as compared to the householders' kilowatt or thousand-watt unit) in 1960 to 4,350,000 in 1965. This last figure represents only about 0.4 percent of our total power output. It has been estimated that by the year 2000 about 10 percent of our power will be generated in nuclear-fueled plants, and that the use of power will increase somewhere between 25- and 200-fold. In other words the use of nuclear power will grow at least to 625 or possibly to 5000 times present levels.

It does not take any great mathematical ability to see that in the future we will be burying or dumping at sea fantastic amounts of radioactive wastes. Experts do not seem concerned by the prospect, but the potentiality for serious radioactive pollution becomes really alarming. *There will be no room at all for carelessness or miscalculation.* Radioactivity causes genetic damage that can have no other effect than to add to the future numbers of humans crippled by such genetic diseases as diabetes, gout, sickle-cell anemia, and phenylketonuria. We already know of over 1500 such congenital flaws of the human!

So far, in the handling of radioactivity, we seem to have exercised great precaution. The advice of scientists has largely been followed, and, though there are those who are worried even today that we may be causing irretrievable trouble for the future, the majority of experts seems satisfied. Industrial use of radioactivity has been firmly regulated. But what of the future? One wonders, as the population of the United States grows and demands more and more power per capita, whether the voice of scientific caution will continue to be heard. On several occasions already enthusiasts for the use of nuclear devices for huge scale blasting have been contained only by the organized arousing of the scientific community. And what will happen when power-hungry countries regard industrial development as more important than solicitude for their downstream neighbors? Communist China, for example, has shown no concern whatsoever for the pollution of the atmosphere caused by her bomb testing. As we escalate the use of nuclear power all over the world, these problems will all too soon cease to be academic. The only cheering prospect is that fusion power processes—if they prove possible—will essentially eliminate the problem of radioactive spent fuel.

Thermal Pollution

Far above Cayuga's waters
There's an awful smell. . . .
—TRADITIONAL

STILL ANOTHER BY-PRODUCT of human activity deserves consideration. A great deal of water is used for cooling. Generally this water is not harmed except that the heat is transferred—for example—from a chemical reactor or an electric generating plant to water that is allowed to return to the run-off cycle. In most instances we have not worried about the resultant increase in temperature of a river or estuary. After all, it soon cools off by radiation and evaporation. But ecologists point out (while the industry vigorously denies) that many instances can be cited in which the entire character of an environment has been altered because of man-made local temperature increases of even a few degrees. The temperature of the enormous Columbia River has been raised appreciably by the Hanford nuclear reactor. A current fight of Congress vs. the AEC concerns the already abused Connecticut River and the plans of a power company to establish a fission-fueled generating plant on its banks. The opinion has been expressed, after investigation by Senator Muskie's Pollution Committee, that the temperature of this river will be raised (I assume fairly locally) fifteen to twenty degrees, causing total destruction of the present plant and animal populations. There are numerous examples of rivers whose biology has been thrown badly out of balance by the heat from our present comparatively small, fossil-fueled power plants.

Cornell University, as every collegiate beer-bibber knows, lies high above Cayuga's waters. Now it is claimed that the entire Lake Cayuga, serving as one of the state's prime recreational areas, is threatened by the proposed construction of an 830-megawatt, nuclear-fueled power plant. Even though the lake is thirty-eight miles long, up to 435 feet deep, and naturally cold, a group of Cornell biologists has warned that the waste heat will speed up eutrophication causing growth of algae that will convert Cayuga to a "diluted pea soup."

A most acrimonious controversy ensued in which the opponents of the biologists not only failed to refute their arguments but simply countered with cynical statements that "you can't stop progress" and that maybe the power plant would provide a "unique opportunity to study the effects of thermal pollution." According to an article in *Science*, it became apparent that the power company had given no attention to the possible ecological effects of thermal pollution nor even of the release of slightly radioactive waste products into the lake and atmosphere. Finally a plan was worked out by which the power company would support a biological study at a cost of $135,000 for a period of a year to eighteen months and other physical studies raising the total research cost to $500,000. It has been agreed by relatively disinterested people that the result may indeed justify construction of the power plant. But the apparent fact is that allegedly construction was all but underway without the giving of any adequate consideration to the possible ecological consequences in one of New York's most famed and beautiful recreational lakes. I think we may be sure that Cayuga will not be unique as a threatened lake. We can only hope that as the result of this controversy we shall be able to take a more rational approach—from both sides—in the future.

Heat pollution of bays, estuaries, and even coastal waters, incredible as it may seem, is a distinct prospect. The demands of nuclear power plants for cooling are inherently 50 percent greater, per unit of capacity, than those of conventional generators. To be competitive and efficient, present plans call for enormous installations, with capacities in the 1000–3000 megawatt range compared to the usual 100–700 megawatt capacity of present-day plants. It is said that power production will use the equivalent of 50 percent of our total run-off water by 1980 and two-thirds by the year 2000. Obviously this far exceeds the capacities of our rivers as sources of cooling. In addition to providing cooling, ocean water can be a source of by-product desalinated fresh water, as we have seen. Available data show, however, that with installations of the size contemplated we cannot simply assume that the heated, concentrated brine returned to the ocean will mix harmlessly and be carried away from our coast. On the contrary it is obvious that each proposed nuclear power plant must be located with great care and that a considerable amount of reasearch will be required to show that the biological effects of heat and increased salt concentration will be negligible, local, or at least not unduly destructive.

It has been seriously proposed that benefits may ensue. Warming of the Savannah River is expected to aid the vanishing alligator. There are allegedly prospects of considerable benefit from warm water irrigation of food crops, and studies are underway. A raising of the coastal water temperature of Maine has been touted as improving the breeding of lobsters, and it is claimed that oyster spawning might be increased in Long Island Sound from a yearly period of three months to one of ten months as a result of the heat discharge from a proposed plant. My personal opinion is that raising the temperature of Maine coastal swimming water can be nothing other than an improvement, but there are those ingrained masochists who would disagree.

The important point is that this entire area of human alteration of our water environment is suddenly upon us, and we lack the data for sound judgment. The long-term effects may be harmless or even beneficial, but it makes an ecologist nervous as a cat on a tin roof when balances are upset with unpredictable results. As we saw when we discussed pesticides, quite alarming things with far-reaching ramifications can happen from seemingly trivial beginnings. Although much more attention is currently being paid to this area of biology, it is obvious that we have only scratched the surface of Pandora's box.

Solid Wastes

In addition to the problems of pollution of the atmosphere and our natural waters, we are increasingly confronting the impossibility of adequate disposal of our solid wastes. The present solutions amount to adding the pollution of land to that of water and air. In the United States today nearly everything is individually handsomely packaged. The information explosion (plus trash mail) fills our mailboxes with paper products and, as is well known, we discard per capita more food as garbage than many people have available for total sustenance. The result is about six pounds of solid waste per person per day or, when industrial and agricultural trash is included, a total of about 3.5 *billion tons* per year to be disposed of at a cost that has been estimated at $4.5 *billion.*

There are a number of problems in addition to that of the total bulk. The Department of Health, Education, and Welfare has estimated that 94 percent of the 12,000 disposal sites in current use are unacceptable. The "sanitary land-fill" type of operation has been highly touted, but suffers from the large percentage of the trash that consists of packaging and plastics that neither compact well nor decay in a reasonable time. Municipal incinerators can operate with a much greater efficiency than individual trash burners, but at best they add appreciably to air pollution, unavoidably add to the carbon dioxide content of the air, and leave solid residues that must be gotten rid of. And the main difficulty with burning, of course, is that a lot of the trash is not readily burnable. This includes each year in the United States some 7 million discarded automobiles, 55 billion cans, 23 billion bottles, not to mention baby carriages, bicycles, Barbie dolls, bathroom scales, and ball point pens. In many municipalities, strong efforts have been made to force the householder to separate the burnables from nonburnables. In most places large nonburnable objects—such as discarded bicycles or lawnmowers—are refused altogether. Confronted with such inevitable discards, the already harassed taxpayer has had to hunt up private trash haulers. In my home town Christmas trees are collected but only on certain specified dates; in other cities garbage must be wrapped and kept separate from the rest of the trash. Not only do such strictures anger the taxpayer, who feels with some justification that he has better things to do than sort trash and lug three or four containers to and from the curb on schedule each week, they have largely proved unenforceable. More and more people have taken the easy way of dumping the more embarrassing junk in the nearest vacant lot by the dark of the moon. The Bloomington, Indiana, city fathers spent $300,000 on an incinerator, several years listening to the complaints of the trash collectors and taxpayers, thousands of dollars each year on up-keep and repairs of supposedly modern equipment that kept breaking down, month after month listening to the complaints about the stench from those who lived nearby, and then finally gave up. The incinerator simply did not do the job and it has been closed. We have gone back essentially to the city dump solution—now glorified by renaming it a "sanitary land-fill." The local Board of Health has refused repeatedly to regard the dump as sanitary and to renew its license. Meanwhile a local entrepreneur, outside the city limits, happily devotes his back forty to private dumping, charges more each year, and fills the sky with stench and smoke from his burning. His cows root happily in the garbage and industrial trash, and discomfited citizens, who come with trash for lack of any other solution, wonder uneasily if their kids are drinking milk from the garbage-fed cows. Everyone is pretty unhappy, the papers continually print complaints and stories of angry fights between the Board of Health and County Council, and the trash piles up. These difficulties would be more entertaining if they were not so frustrating. We have been seeking a solution in this small community for a decade or more and seem no closer than ever. If anything things are steadily worse, and we are by no means exceptional.

In San Francisco for 100 years the accepted practice has been to use trash to fill the supposedly less desirable margins of the famous bay. After more than 280 square miles had been filled, reducing the Bay area by one-third, it began to be realized that not only were the "useless" marshes and mudflats essential to the ecology of a number of marine and bird species, they played a vital role in combatting pollution through the activities of algae and bacteria that lived in these shallow waters. It was also realized that further reduction of the bay might have a disastrous and irreversible effect on the Bay Area's celebrated climate, since the Bay waters acted as a heat sink and humidifier. Albert Miller, a climatologist at San Jose State College, has said, for example, "If twenty-five percent of the existing bay were filled, temperature could increase at the bay's south end by five degrees in summer and decrease as much as three degrees in winter." Rainfall patterns would change in the entire area. Further filling of the Bay was sharply protested by many citizens' groups and it is believed that the situation will be controlled by state legislation passed in 1969. New York City for years dumped its trash at sea by the thousands of tons a day, but a large part of it found its way back to the neighboring shore area, and the United States Supreme Court forbade the practice in 1936. Indianapolis, a city of about half a million, has been ringed with smouldering, stinking dumps for as long as I have lived in the state. The billowing smoke could be seen for miles and frequently blew over the downtown area. Now a city ordinance forbids the burning of trash. But what to do with it? The most likely, if incredible, solution seems to be shipping the trash elsewhere, and the city fathers are talking glibly of sending it to "southern Indiana," which is where I live. San Francisco and Philadelphia are right now resorting to rail shipment. Some solution!

The fact is that the disposal of refuse and garbage, like every problem that is tied to population and urbanization, is growing steadily more difficult. As with other problems that we have considered (most notably water, mineral, and energy consumption) this one is increasing faster than the population. In the early 1960's it was said that refuse accumulated at a per capita rate of four pounds a day in the United States. A recent estimate, made public by President Nixon, cites a current figure of six pounds a day and a projection to 1980 of eight. Again we see a compounded rate of exponential increase.

The nature of trash, moreover, has changed drastically in this century. Tires, bottles, and cans cannot be left to decay by natural processes, since it will take roughly forever—at least with bottles. Many plastics have been designed to be highly rot resistant and often burn with the production of highly noxious fumes. An ideal solution for garbage seemed to be the invention of the ever-more-popular individual sink disposals, but this elimination of the stinking and unsanitary garbage can has come at the price of a greatly increased burden on already overloaded municipal sewage treatment plants. In many places the resultant load of organic material in the poorly treated sewage winds up by increasing intolerably the oxygen deficit in rivers and estuaries and hence straining far beyond their limits the natural disposal processes that depend on other forms of life.

My Scottish heredity and frugal New England upbringing incline me to agree most emphatically with those who believe that we not only can no longer afford to pollute our environment with our trash, we can no longer afford to cast away enormous amounts of organic matter, nitrogen, phosphorus, minerals, etc. Yet no really practical and economical methods of recovery and reuse have appeared. Composting (enthusiasts to the contrary notwithstanding) has repeatedly been found to be impractical and uneconomical. The city of Houston has a huge composting operation that is said to be very successful, but the type of compost that results from municipal waste can be regarded only as a soil conditioner, not (despite popular belief) a magical fertilizer. A large part of the problem with such reconversion processes is separation of the trash. The householder cannot really be expected to do the job; the city cannot afford to make several types of collection even if he could. Most processes that accept everything involve huge installations, unsuited to the village, town, or even small city, and have proved very costly—so far. As with many of our problems we may soon find ourselves unable .to afford the luxury of worrying about the cost.

There are possible solutions in the offing. One, developed at the University of Missouri, converts discarded tires and bottles— two of our most troublesome refuse items—into "glasphalt," a granular filler that has so far stood up very well in test pavement. At Texas A & M a process of incorporating old tires into asphalt is said to increase its flexibility and resistance to cracking. In several European countries trash has been burned to produce electricity, and a large-scale plant being built outside London will handle 1333 tons of crude refuse a day, generate twenty-five to thirty-five megawatts of electricity, and reduce the rubbish to one-tenth of its original volume. The net operation is expected to yield a profit of about $750,000 a year. The Japanese are successfully burning trash to produce both electricity and compressed blocks of building material.

A far-off solution that has been proposed for fusion power plants introduces trash of all kinds into the nuclear plasma at a temperature of 50 *million* degrees centigrade, thereby reducing it to its original elements. In this very complex and still completely theoretical process, it is claimed that all of the materials, including metals that now go completely to waste, would be recovered with no net cost. The enthusiastic proponents have set the year 2000 as a possible goal for this process, but it should be pointed out that we are far from sure that fusion power can be realized at all, far less at a date in the immediate future.

Meanwhile we continue to burn, bury, tax, and pollute. We lug our trash to the curb, the trash collector—if he decides not to strike for better wages for a most disagreeable job—picks it up, throws the can at our dog, and reduces the lid if not the whole can to a battered piece of trash that he then refuses to accept because it cannot be put into a trash can. Our highways become public dumping grounds, our rivers disgusting sludges of slowly decaying organic matter, our parks a site of grim competition between the littering public and litter collectors. Why isn't there a better way? After all, if we can put man on the moon. . . . But I am sorry you have reminded me of this, since what we have done so far is to land on the moon, a guaranteed completely trash-free primitive area, and litter it with tons of junk—a monument to mankind that will last essentially for eternity.

Noise Pollution

The proof that Americans are a tolerant people
is that the inventor of the juke box died a natural death.
—Author unknown

A RELATIVE NEWCOMER to the pollution field is noise —or at least our concern about noise. One difficulty in this area is that of definition. Noise is generally defined as an undesired sound, but this is at best subjective, since what is delightful music to teenagers is unbearable noise to me. In fact I suspect that it is bearable to teenagers only because of the repeatedly demonstrated fact that they are joyously deafening themselves. In recent articles, *The Sciences* has summarized interesting studies in this area. A number of audiologists have noted that the sound levels (let us call them) of many rock bands are in the range known to cause permanent deafness. Guinea pigs exposed to eighty-eight hours of discotheque-level rock music showed destruction of ear cells. Examination of college freshmen at the University of Tennessee revealed hearing losses in over 25 percent of the group examined; the hearing of some of the students had been reduced to that of an average sixty-five-year-old. Who knows, the communications gap between generations may be due to the fact that we just don't shout loud enough.

But adult city dwellers are also in trouble. It has long been accepted that constant exposure to noise—as in numerous heavy industries—causes deafness. Jet aircraft, pneumatic hammers, subway trains, heavy truck traffic, and many other common noise makers have been shown to produce sound at a level permanently damaging to those closely and constantly exposed. *The Sciences* attributes to former Surgeon General William Stenert the statement that, "Between 6 and 16 million Americans are losing their hearing to occupational noise." Meanwhile, the noise level in urban residential neighborhoods is said to be rising at one decibel per year, and as for downtown, "although industrial noise levels exceeding 85 decibels are known to be injurious to health, ordinary community noise often surpasses this level of loudness." Dr. Samuel Rosen of Mt. Sinai Hospital in New York found that, "In relatively quiet societies, such as the Maban tribe in southeastern Sudan, tribesmen in their seventies generally hear as well as New Yorkers in their twenties."

Hearing loss is not the only possible result. A number of investigators have shown that quite measurable physiological shock-like effects are attributable to sudden noises. It has been suggested that the booms from supersonic airplanes may trigger heart attacks in the susceptible. Rabbits, after eight weeks of exposure to high noise levels, showed long-term effects to the vascular system including higher cholesterol levels and increased atherosclerosis (hardening of the arteries). Exposure of rats to intense noise resulted in a variety of symptoms, including homosexual behavior! Now a parent can lie awake at night worrying over whether his teenage children will go deaf or turn queer first and hoping he won't get a heart attack when he receives the news.

Finally come the more subtle and questionable but possibly most important effects of noise on personality as a result of continuous, low-level (at least not physiologically damaging) exposure. It has not infrequently been proposed that the traditional irritableness of many city dwellers is the result of chronic exposure to noise. Since noise is only a part of the stress on those who live or work in our high pressure cities, it is difficult to distinguish various causes, and a satisfactorily controlled experimental group is nearly impossible to find or create. Still there is the suspicion that noise is important. *The Sciences* quotes *Medical News* as reporting that Caracas, Venezuela is one of the noisiest cities in the world and that "the terrible noise has turned citizens from happy, friendly people into grouchy people who generally also suffer from poor hearing."

But noise pollution has one comforting aspect. If the human race succeeds in destroying itself one way or another, we may leave behind a world almost totally unfit for anyone or anything to live in, but at least it will be nice and quiet.

THE PROSPECTS

Most certainly alas!   Always, always.
— A E S C H Y L U S, *The Persians*

ONE WOULD LIKE TO CONCLUDE this gloomy discussion of pollution by pointing with *Readers-Digest* pride at the salutary results of antipollutionary, organized citizen action in restoring Great Neck Bay, or somewhere, to a scene of rural beauty. So far as I can read, it ain't so, though people are at the moment mightily aroused. One hopes that the excitement about pollution will not backlash when the bills begin to come in. But progress is slow because pollution control involves vested interests of several kinds. One is the industrial pollutor who will have to invest money to decrease pollutionary contributions. We recently had a splendid local example. After several sewer lids popped elegantly into the air to the amazement and discomfiture of passersby, it was discovered that the whole sewer system of one end of town contained an explosive, solvent air mixture. A considerable amount of publicity and investigation finally pinpointed the industrial source from which, during the several weeks of investigation, solvents continued to flow. Finally the industry (never publicly identified) threatened openly to leave town if this "continual harassment" did not stop, but it has been noted that while no responsibility was ever admitted, the dumping has mysteriously ceased. Unfortunately this example could be multiplied n-fold; industries first disclaiming all responsibility, usually then claiming the pollutant is harmless, finally saying that they will have to go out of business if saddled with the costs of anti-pollutionary measures. And the fact is that in some cases it will undoubtedly be true.

In addition to industry, pollution also involves millions of taxpayers who may hate pollution like sin, but who hate higher taxes even more. Money for adequate municipal or individual sewage systems usually comes pretty hard. Almost everyone is willing to pay what he must for water fit to drink, but to pay to avoid giving the guy down the river a little trouble—that is another question. Christian philosophy and the love of one's neighbor do not seem to extend far downstream.

One can cite some positive examples such as ORSANCO, which has achieved enormous progress in cleaning the Ohio. Not that the Ohio can be bottled raw to make baby formula, but the level of treatment of incoming sewage *has* been raised from 1 to over 95 percent and many obnoxious industrial sources have been shut off. They have a long way to go, but at least the Ohio is better than it was and is more than holding its own in the face of increasing industrialization along its banks. We have already mentioned progress along the Raritan and the huge Federal program, subsidized by tax expenditures that will eventually reach into the billions, in an effort to save the Great Lakes. Lake Washington has been rescued, San Francisco Bay has been saved from being buried alive, early alarm is being expressed for many lakes including Tahoe. I am sure that with current public arousal to the dangers and extent of pollution there will be many others. The techniques are largely available, it is simply a matter of facing the facts and spending the money.

Air pollution is another matter. One can point with pride to

St. Louis. But there the cause was readily assignable to cheap Illinois coal in common use. It proved relatively easy to pass laws forbidding the use of this out-of-state product; I suspect it would have been a far different matter had local industry been involved. St. Louis had been a notoriously horrible example (with traffic policemen deserting their posts in the middle of the street in broad daylight for the simple reason that they were invisible to motorists). Now it is just another member (in 1967, tenth) of the long list of polluted cities. In Los Angeles, at the other end of the scale, frantic effort over some twenty-five years has just about achieved a stand-off—the industrial sources, dumps, and home burning have been nearly eliminated but replaced by the automobile. Beyond any doubt whatsoever the petroleum-powered motor vehicle is now the prime and least controllable source of pollution in the United States, and no one pretends that the average citizen is going to be willing to part with it until he is presented with an equivalent or better alternative. Unfortunately we have built our entire economy, not to say virtually our civilization, around the automobile.

Surely we can devise ways to get rid of solid wastes. Unlike the problems of the automobile, we do not seem to need any real breakthrough in technology, only the willingness to spend the money to develop the engineering and to find the most economical processes. Not that this will be easy, but it is being done even now. Although there are as many producers of solid trash as automobile users, we have long been organized to handle this problem. One is dealing with a few thousand muncipalities, not a hundred million motor vehicles.

I begin to see the glimmerings of the idea that it may be inadvisable in the long run to throw away our resources of nitrates, phosphates, metals, fossil fuels, etc. It seems to me that here it is largely a matter of equating cost with need and with acceptance of the idea that we cannot continue to waste and pollute regardless of cost. A few scientists, at least, are worried about the long-term effects of the current and increasing pollution of our entire atmosphere and our oceans. We have made deleterious changes already, the hope is that they are not yet too serious and that we will stop polluting soon enough.

And this brings us to the question of what constitutes soon enough. What are we willing to accept as the pollutionary cost of an ever expanding, ever urbanizing human race? Do we want, for example, swimmable or drinkable lake and river waters or just water that can be *made* drinkable? How much increment to the death rate are we willing to accept as the result of air pollution? Unfortunately we often do not know where we are, far less where we want to be in terms of pollution of this or that kind in this or that area. We can improve. But if you asked me to describe a *single* city that had been grossly air-polluted and was now enjoying fresh, country air, or a single example of a stream or lake or estuary that had been grossly polluted and that has now been restored to pristine condition—forget it. I do not see the slightest indication that we can hope to do much more than keep things from getting worse as the population increases, urbanizes, and industrializes. Despite a great deal of publicity, not to say propaganda, against pollution of air and water, the general public attitude toward controlling the basic cause, population, seems to be summarized in the punch line of the classical pollutionary joke, "Don't make waves."

7 /

Competitors

Oh give me a home
Where the buffalo roam
And the deer and the antelope play.

—DR. BREWSTER HIGLEY

A FACTOR IN THE CONTROL OF NATURAL POPULATIONS is often the competitor or predator. As the lemmings wax and wane, so do the white foxes and martens that lunch upon them. The local owls, hawks, and even reindeer fatten on the horde at its peak. Similar relationships between insect cycles and those of insectivorous birds are well known; many other examples could be cited, as the occurrence of influenza virus vs. the level of general population, or the ratio of friendly loan agencies to poor people.

With the human, so far, the competitor relationship has been pretty much all one way. Of course, the cave man, surprised by a saber-toothed tiger as he dragged his little sugar plum home by the hair, may have found things very sticky indeed. I have often wondered whether she got up and helped hubby give the tiger his knocks and then lay down to be dragged the rest of the way home or whether she pitched in on the tiger's side. It is hard to see how she could do either or neither without losing face. Still, things progressed, steel was invented, and even the fabulous dragon succumbed to St. George.

7. / Competitors

Ordinarily we think of man as having got the upper hand only with the invention of gunpowder. This may be a misapprehension. Numerous mysteries of biological history surround the extinction of various animals that seemed to be doing reasonably well. A recently published theory suggests that one after another of ancient species succumbed not to some mysterious vagary of nature but to man, as he learned to cooperate in the hunt and as he developed even rather crude weapons. It is believed, for example, that the elephant and mastodon in North America fell victim to our predecessors. But certainly with the invention and perfection of the gun, the pattern became unmistakable. In the United States we have seen the innumerable passenger pigeon totally destroyed within the memory of our fathers. I have before me a list of twenty-two species of birds that today are bucking to join the dodo, the Carolina parakeet, the Labrador duck, the great auk, and well over 100 other species known to have become recently extinct. The very symbol of the United States, the bald eagle, trembles on the brink.

Birds are not alone. Although publicized by the often mawkish sentimentalists of the Audubon Society far beyond any reasonable significance, they are merely the most observed and perhaps illogically mourned of our vanishing species. The buffalo, whose hordes were the Indian's endless resource and an unbelievable feature of pioneering days, has been saved through last minute action and lives today as a protected curiosity. A similar European animal, the aurochs, is but a memory. The most magnificent and harmless of mammals, the useful blue whale, is disappearing as fast as greedy man can accomplish the deed; modern efficiency has apparently reduced his future to a matter of a few years. In Africa, a land commonly thought of as primitive and teeming with game, a number of species live only because of intensive efforts at protection. Most of the large game animals are in real trouble—the rhinoceros because his horn, powdered, is believed by the Chinese to be a magical aphrodisiac. (And who knows, perhaps that is why we are predicting a billion Chinese by the year 2000.) The peaceable gorilla is likely to bite the dust soon as a result of the encroachments of expanding African agriculture, and others of the large primates are not far behind. Appreciable inroads have been made on the seemingly limitless populations of smaller monkeys by demands for their kidneys for tissue culture of polio vaccine. Numerous species of South American reptiles, birds, and mammals are falling victim to our demands for exotic skins, furs, and even pets. Unbelievably, the last few dodos were slain to become museum specimens. And so goes the ever lengthening list of animals threatened or destroyed by man.

Extinction is, of course, an inevitable feature of evolution. Although this book is written with the feeling that man may join the list and that it is, perhaps, unrealistic to try to stay the process, it seems natural to want to cling on, anachronistic and destructive though we may be. One danger that exists, at the moment, is obviously our ability to upset the balance of nature to our own personal disadvantage. It seems as though man is doing far more than his share in hurrying evolution along. North America formerly teemed with game. Today a very high proportion of our population has never seen in nature an animal larger than a rabbit. We have grown so contemptuous of wild creatures that a considerable problem in Yellowstone Park is the number of tourists who try to treat bears and deer as Disneyesque household pets. They focus their cameras happily as they send their toddlers, with a bag of candy in one hand and an offering of a single piece in the other, up to a 300 pound bear. Recently two girls were attacked and killed by grizzly bears in Glacier National Park. National headlines resulted, which seems to me to show a lot of anthropocentric gall considering that over 20,000 bears are killed in the United States each year by hunters. In zoos the principal problem is not nearly so much to protect the public from the ferocious beasts as vice versa.

The point I am trying to make is that man, today, has little to fear from anything bigger than himself. Our enemies now come largely from the other end of the scale. The rat, at a present population of 3 billion, plies his insidious trade at incredible expense to our increasingly precious stocks of food. In Bombay alone it is estimated that rats each month destroy the equivalent of 1500 to 1600 sacks of grain, enough to feed one-fifth of the city. The meek and lowly insect, despite our massive campaigns with ever more successful insecticides, destroys even more food. D. M. DeLong, an entomologist at Ohio State, says, "Insects eat, steal, or destroy ⅓ of everything which man grows and stores for the future." The insect also demonstrates an adaptability and multiplicity of species that suggests to many entomologists that he may indeed inherit the earth if we manage to kill ourselves off by one or another application of massive stupidity. And both rats and insects contribute importantly to the spread of pathogenic bacteria and viruses—enemies always awaiting a chance.

As with the bear, we have come to treat the microbial pathogen with little respect. Secure in the faith that the United States Public Health Service, the Pure Food and Drug people, the American Medical Association, and our probably overworked and certainly overpaid family doctors are looking out for us, we stumble along with the conviction that disease is licked or nearly so. We speak confidently of the total elimination of malaria, yellow fever, smallpox, polio, and measles. But it is surprising how small a disruption of organized society is required to open the door to epidemic and mass death. Earthquakes, avalanches, tsunamis, hurricanes, garbage strikes, riots, and wars all carry the threat of sudden disaster from such well-known and ancient enemies as typhoid, cholera, typhus, plague, and dysentery. Any situation in which people become intensely crowded is potentially dangerous. If malnutrition or starvation are piled on top, even fairly ordinary diseases can become threatening. When the ordinary principles of public health are neglected in addition, whether because of indifference, as in prisons or refugee camps, or of social disruption, massive disease is an obvious consequence. And these possibilities become very real as population increases, famine threatens, and humans crowd into the cities in slums and ghettoes. If, as has been frequently predicted, the world erupts into an ever increasing ferment of riots or actual wars between the haves and have-nots, it is far from inconceivable that the control of disease that we take so much for granted may easily break down on a massive scale. In many natural animal societies, disease plays a key, if secondary, role in population crashes. In the Middle Ages, plague caused the sole important decline in the rate of increase of the human race.

Et Tu Brute?

       To BE REALISTIC, however, one must face the clear fact that man, alone among the inhabitants of earth, is by all odds his own worst enemy. Other animals indeed indulge in individual combat. Fights for the favors of the opposite sex are common to many species, as are those to establish the comfortable pecking order that serves as the basis for the social structure of many flock or herd animals. Individual struggles to establish territorial rights are now thought of as fundamental to great numbers of species. My understanding, however, is that these fights, while often fierce, are seldom to the death. Once social hegemony has been established, the vanquished removes himself to live to fight another day or even, in many instances, philosophically takes his position in the hierarchy. A half-century of personal observation affirms this statement with respect, at least, to the dog. Booth Tarkington first brought to my attention, in *Penrod*, the fact that any dog, no matter how puny and ancient, is unalterably convinced that in his own yard he can lick any other dog no matter how fearsome. The incredible thing, as I have seen again and again even with our own outsized Labrador, is that the other dog believes it too.

7. / *Competitors*

Some of the more organized social insects indulge in wars of mutual destruction, but this behavior is seemingly rare. Man is essentially unique in his persistent attempts, throughout history, to exterminate his fellow in massive groups. Clan Fraser and, by extension, I exist allegedly only because the neighborly Campbells neglected or at least failed to kill off the women of the Fraser group who had thoughtfully gotten themselves pregnant before their heroes sallied forth to tribal combat in the Scottish Highlands. Of course, it is possible that certain of the ladies sought other comforts later, but one draws the veil over such primitive horrors with their implications of the sullying of the stock. One cannot read history without at least conceiving of the notion that battle and war have, through the ages, been more an outlet for excess manly energy than anything else. No doubt Menelaus was vexed when the Trojans made off with Helen, but in even a casual perusal of Homer one can but note the ease with which the Greek heroes gracefully adapted themselves to life with various ladies who crossed their paths and the even greater ease with which a personal fit of pique developed into national slaughter.

Today's wars are over far more serious matters, such as which of two groups of scoundrels shall rule and rob a nation that, by and large, could not care less. And as befits the immensity of the issues, we now possess the capability to vaporize each other by the tens—nay hundreds—of millions. Fortunately, the production of these weapons requires great sophistication and industrial organization, with the result, so far, that by the time the politicians and military have them at hand the people have become too prosperous to be interested in self-annihilation. The Chinese, of course, have placed nuclear weapons far ahead of food and other niceties. They may indeed find an ideological cause worthy of button pushing, even though it seems difficult to understand how a nation that desperately needs to be fed and modernized will gain through the total destruction of another that has, undestroyed, the potentiality, and probably even the willingness, to solve a great many of these problems for it.

Although we are far afield, one last word on man's potential inhumanity to man. Assuming, as in the movie *Dr. Strangelove*, that we may "get our hair mussed" in a nuclear war and lose a few dozen million people, it does seem pertinent to speculate whether this might prove a solution to our problem. The answer, as usual, is equivocal.

The world population is now about 3.5 billion. Estimates presented to the United States Congress have suggested that something like 70 million people in this country might be killed as a direct result of a good old, all-out nuclear war between Russia and us. Now, of course, we are not just going to sit here. The military, in their protected lairs, will push our buttons too and, with a little luck, will certainly kill an equal number of Russians. So we have about 140 million dead. This, apparently, we have come to accept as a possible consequence of our arms race—a bizarre commentary on a nation that weeps at Lassie movies, and mobilizes from coast to coast, spending tens of thousands of dollars, to rescue a child trapped in a well. But no stranger, perhaps, than the fact that we have calmly accepted 50,000 dead a year from the automobile. Let us not boggle over numbers and ethical principles. We are seeking practical solutions to important problems. Let us assume that our rulers, in their wisdom, precipitate a war over the question of whether a trawler (translated: "spy ship") was one-tenth of a mile within or without the territorial limit, and let us suppose that a *billion* people are killed either as a direct result or because of the subsequent disruption of civilized life with famine and disease. We are reduced from 3.5 to 2.5 billion people. At the present rate of growth this would delay the approaching population disaster by just seventeen years. That we could murder a billion people and recover before our infants marry may seem incredible, yet it is an inevitable consequence of the exponential nature of the expansion of the human race.

One can argue that a nuclear war that exterminates a billion humans will so disrupt civilization that we shall never recover. The point, however, is that if any substantial, organized, and highly developed group—say the Australians, as in *On the Beach*—remained undisturbed, recovery would be remarkably rapid. Reducing the entire human race to 11.4 million Australians (about one-tenth the estimated world population at the birth of Christ) and recommencing with a thirty-five year doubling time, we would restore our present numbers in less than 300 years. The real point is that we cannot help the population problem by reducing the *numbers* of humans. We can remedy the situation only by reducing the *rate of doubling;* that is to say the birth rate minus death rate. Eventually the two must be brought into balance and the population stabilized.

Summary

Pressure from competitors, a factor often controlling the growth of natural populations, does not seem likely to place a limit on the expansion of the human race unless we abet the competitors by our own stupidity. We exercise ruthless control over all species except our own. Even a massive epidemic or an all-out nuclear war with extermination of a large part of the race will not help unless as a result the *rate* of expansion is strongly cut; that is to say unless we are forced to retreat to a primitive way of life with a high death rate.

Part III

Population

Control

8 /

Birth, Population, and Death

The owl looked up to the stars above
And sang to a small guitar...

—LEAR

SEVERAL FACTS THAT CONFRONT US are inescapable:
1. Man has changed the face of the earth. Of all creatures that have ever lived, man has had more effect on the planet in a shorter time than any other. In the past hundred years we have significantly altered the composition of the entire atmosphere, polluted a major part of the available fresh water, used much of the fossil fuel laid down over millions of years, converted to food or other human use a large proportion of the available dry land, consumed or at least rearranged a considerable fraction of high grade mineral deposits, changed drastically the character and distribution of other biological species. In the next hundred years even greater changes are bound to occur.
2. The human race is not only expanding in numbers exponentially—that is to say in a geometrical progression by a process of doubling—but, even worse, *super*-exponentially, since the doubling time becomes ever shorter. In the last one-tenth of one percent of our existence (the two millennia of the Christian era) it has dropped from well over a thousand years to thirty-five years and continues to shrink as death rates all over the world decrease.
3. No population, be it of bacteria, insects, lemmings, deer, or

191

humans can continue exponential expansion indefinitely. But the human race, with a few relatively minor setbacks due to epidemics (for example, plague) has increased steadily for several thousand—perhaps a million—years. That this trend must change is inevitable, the only questions are when, why, and with what eventual result.

4. Of the factors known to limit populations, several (available space, food, water, mineral resources, accumulated waste products, catastrophic wars) threaten to curtail human expansion either in a matter of a decade (as with food) or within a few hundred years at the most.

5. Urbanization, industrialization, and increases in the material standard of living have compounded many of our demands. In the United States our high animal protein diet leads to very large per capita requirements for space and water. Our use of metered water, per person, is also increasing at an alarming rate. Industry and air conditioning account for some of the increment, but food production depends more and more on irrigation, which even now accounts for a large fraction of our metered water. We also see ever larger individual use of paper and paper products, petroleum, and metals of nearly every kind. The energy requirements of the United States citizen have risen precipitously in this century and show no signs of levelling off.

6. All of these factors have contributed to pollution of the air, fresh and salt water, and even of our land environment.

7. The development of other nations will inevitably result in strong acceleration of parallel demands and concomitant potentiality for environmental deterioration all over the world.

8. With respect to most of these factors, no firm predictions of eventual limits on population or development can be made because of the possibility of temporizing compromises. Most "solutions" will result in a decrease in the material standard of living as we in the United States now picture it. We *can* eat

processed alfalfa, algae, or bacteria. We *can* live in apartments at a population density like that of Hong Kong. We *can* accept increasing pollution of the environment as a fact of (a shortened) life or control it at rapidly increasing expense. We *can* recover minerals for a long time with ever decreasing yields. Etc.

9. The ultimate basis for all of these problems lies in population. We have the choice between adapting our numbers to our resources and environment or attempting the reverse. All of the possibilities for modifying the environment to *our* needs only delay the day when the human population—like all biological populations—will expand to the limit of some important controlling factor. Not at all impossibly we may then face a catastrophic, conceivably total, collapse of the race.

Obviously, we must use all possible means to postpone trouble; equally clearly we shall very soon need long-term solutions to an increasing variety of problems. Unfortunately we are a long way from persuading most people and most nations of the necessity for action and cooperation. Unlike any other creature, alive or extinct, the human has the mental ability, social organization, and scientific capacity to solve problems of overuse of the environment by management of excessive birth rates. One wonders how many or how great disasters will be required to convince us to take a world-wide view of the problem of population control.

It seems all too likely that instead of facing the question while it is still answerable in reasonable terms, we are going to muddle along, compromising the desirable with the necessary, in an infinite number of small decisions or forced situations until we are reduced to a state that we would *now* regard as miserable or intolerable. Perhaps we should begin by facing the fact that the *average* human state is *right now* miserable. Over half of the race is inadequately nourished by any standards. As always, then, "Why don't they do something about it?"

POPULATION CONTROL—WHO WANTS HOW MUCH?

HOW DO PEOPLE FEEL ABOUT BIRTH CONTROL? That eventual stabilization of the human race is an absolute necessity is seemingly news to nearly everyone. Once explained, it makes good long-term sense, but very few people have ever thought about it, far less considered it as something they might have to worry about in their lifetimes. In discussing the problem with a wide sample of people, I find that except for the flaming liberals (convinced, as always, that they are uniquely qualified to run the lives of others) almost everyone is agreed that dictation of family size to the individual by the government is anathema. Yet unless birth rates fall by natural social pressures or by devious *applied* pressures (the possibilities of which we shall consider at the end of this chapter) the temptation to try to control family size by law will be great. I fail completely, however, to see any realistic prospect for world-wide control by agreement. It seems inconceivable that nations unable now to negotiate on international fishing rights (to take a fairly trivial example) will agree on a balance of population in the foreseeable future. It is not beyond the memory of many of us that Hitler and Mussolini saw increased population as a means toward national ends. Sukarno ceaselessly demanded that poverty-stricken Indonesia, with a population in 1961 of less than 100 million, must strive for 400 million. Fortunately, his successors have put social progress first. Mao Tse-tung has been quoted (even by me) as saying that in a nuclear holocaust the survivors of 800 million Chinese could scarcely fail to come out on top. Yet we *must* have a lower world birth rate in the very foreseeable future. My own feeling is that this must come from the persuasion of individuals, not governments.

In the United States, between Roman Catholicism and the remnants of Victorianism, we have considered birth control a forbidden topic. In one of those extraordinary contradictions between private behavior and public image to which the American is so addicted, public discussion was considered taboo long after private practice became nearly universal. According to demographer Judith Blake of the University of California, Berkeley, "Over 95 percent of fecund U.S. couples either use birth-control methods or intend to do so." Even among Catholic couples in the United States, numerous surveys in the 1960's showed that over 50 percent practiced birth control by methods other than the approved rhythm technique. But as Dr. Blake points out in an article in *Science*, "The poor . . . have larger families than the advantaged; they not only use birth-control methods less but they use them less effectively." The question, obviously, is why? The accepted reply has been that they just did not understand the problem or that they were irresponsible or that they lacked access to the necessary, possibly illegal, technique. As Dr. Blake points out, these people have had no trouble obtaining illegal drugs. She suggests a quite different answer, namely, that the poor *want* more children. Among the non-Catholic population she finds that whereas the college-educated, in 1968, considered an average of 3.2 children ideal, the grade-school educated wanted 3.7: similarly the members of the higher income groups wanted 3.2 children, those of the lowest group 3.6. A Gallup poll in 1966 uncovered a parallel distribution among those asked whether birth control pills should be available free to families on relief. The less educated, poorer men were only 39 percent in favor of such a policy compared to the other social extreme, who evinced 82 percent approval of this idea. Women, interestingly, were far less divided in opinion, with a 59 to 76 percent majority favoring the idea. The conclusion, then, is that people in the United States as a whole *want more* than the replacement number of children and the poor and less educated want on the average a half a child per family more than the well-to-do.

Recent observations in India suggest that a similar pattern exists there. It was found that men submitting voluntarily to vasectomy, as part of the government program of birth control, already had an average of 4.5 children. In the IUD (intrauterine device) program in Taiwan, it was found (in a 1966 follow-up study) that less than 12 percent of the women participating had had two children or less, 40 percent already had had five or more. In the Swedish program of condom distribution in Africa similar results were noted—those accepting the offer already had considerable families. The take-home lesson seems clear; programs of birth rate control in a wide variety of countries representing a wide diversity of cultures have shown that zero population growth or even an approach to it is going to require something beyond the availability of adequate birth control technique. People the world over basically seem to *want* several children.

In the underdeveloped countries there are difficulties of many kinds, as we shall see. But there is far from universal agreement that general population control is even desirable. At the conclusion of a discussion of this subject with a group of African journalists, supposedly representing the best in young talent from their countries, I was rather appalled to have several of the men tell me that their problem was *under*-population, that they could develop properly only with many more people. Yet these are countries where the birth rate is unbelievably high, malnutrition the norm, and starvation rampant.

WHO DOESN'T WANT BIRTH CONTROL?

IF WE ARE TO EMBARK on world-wide programs of population control, obviously we need to understand the nature of the obstacles to acceptance and implementation.

The Roman Catholic Church

IT IS TEMPTING, at least in the United States, to blame it all on the Catholic church. As we shall see later, various social influences are far more important. The church is actually only one of many factors. But there are sound grounds for admitting that the Catholics have not helped much.

Recently Pope Paul VI—after several years of study by a papal commission—took the unbelievable step of strongly reaffirming a totally inflexible position against any and all forms of artificial birth control. As an encyclical, his statement has the full weight of papal authority and, so far as I have read, has left no crevice through which technology can insinuate itself. It is very difficult to believe that he will not encounter serious trouble even within the church as a fairly immediate result—in fact rumblings are already quite audible. Strangely, there is complaint from both ends of the theological spectrum. The liberals in the church have for years increasingly taken the position that the church was failing to face a very real, very serious problem of responsibility to the individual Catholic family and to the world community with regard to birth control. A Louis Harris poll as long ago as 1964 reported that three out of five United States Catholics wanted change in the attitude of their church. The conservatives are also seriously concerned, but for quite different reasons. Several surveys, including some made by the church itself, have shown that well over half of young Catholic couples in the United States are practicing birth control in defiance of church law. Intolerable as this may be to the conservatives, they must surely be aware of a fact that I have confirmed repeatedly by conversations with Catholic students—that the priesthood is not only closing its eyes to this disobedience but is frequently actively abetting it.

One devout student, whom I knew well, was quite concerned about the possibility of a pregnancy jeopardizing his obtaining the Ph.D. toward which he had worked for years. He found his priest espousing the rhythm method of contraception but not at all unwilling to give it a little shot in the arm. (It needs it. According to well-accepted figures, this church-approved technique of avoiding coitus during the rather unpredictable period of female fertility results in twenty-four pregnancies per 100 women per year, compared to "the pill" at 0.3.) The pill is forbidden, the priest said, except where such health problems as irregular menstrual cycles are involved. My student quickly discovered that his wife indeed had such a difficulty and received the priest's blessing to use the pill. The medical problem, oddly enough, was alleviated immediately four years later when the student completed his degree and got a good job. Now, in three more years, he has two children.

I am often asked how much damage—aside from the difficulties of individual families—the Catholic position really has done. In *The Silent Explosion*, my colleague and friend Philip Appleman considers this question incisively and brilliantly *in extenso*, and the church comes off very badly indeed. With the best will possible and completely without arguing the merits of the Catholic position, several things must be noted. In many areas of strong Catholic influence, the birth rate is appalling. The various projections made in this book are based on a human doubling time of thirty-five years. A 1966 publication of the United Nations, *World Population Prospects as Assessed in 1963*, predicts that between the year 1965 and the year 2000 (thirty-five years) the population of the eight major world areas is indeed expected to increase by an average of 1.9-fold. One of the highest predictions for any major area is for Latin America, just where Catholicism has its strongest influence. The increase there is expected to be 2.6-fold, corresponding to a doubling time of twenty-five years. As stated by J. M. Stycos in *World Population: The View Ahead*, there is considerable evidence that rebellion exists in Latin America even within the church, but it must be noted sadly that the official position has repeatedly been adamantly reaffirmed. In Europe, by contrast, where Catholicism is taken rather less seriously, the increase is expected to be only by 1.2-fold and in the United States 1.7-fold.

8. / Birth, Population, and Death

One might hope that the United Nations, whose World Health Organization has had such success in lengthening human life, would exert great influence through its Population Division. Because of the unremitting opposition of the Catholic-controlled countries, this group has been forced to restrict its activities exclusively to fact gathering. Ironically, it is very largely these facts and the projections based on them that have pointed up the seriousness of the world problem that the United Nations refuses to face.

In the United States Congress it was long considered, justifiably or not, politically suicidal to fail to support the Catholic position without question. This has led to a virtual crippling of scientific research into methods for effective birth control. A very high percentage of world support for biological and biomedical research comes from the United States Government, mostly from the National Institutes of Health (NIH). Study of contraception, however, has been confined largely to private foundations, pharmaceutical firms, or other nongovernmental institutions. The caution of Federal agencies in allocating funds for anything that could be considered even related to this area has been fanatic. Only very recently has this attitude been relaxed. In 1962 D. S. Greenberg, a staff writer for *Science* magazine, discussed the point as follows: "With considerable justification for wariness . . . public officials generally tend to steer away from the issue [of birth control], which was the case several months ago when the Public Health Service decided that it would not be discreet to release a survey of research and training in population and fertility control in the U.S." Not only could we do essentially nothing, we couldn't even publish the fact that little was being done.

In 1961, of $880 million allocated for the control of disease by the NIH., only $1.3 million, less than two-tenths of one percent, was spent on research related to fertility control. Under President Eisenhower (and before) the Population Division of the United Nations was pointedly not supported. Eisenhower, in 1960, was asked for his position on birth control and replied, "I cannot imagine anything more emphatically a subject that is not a proper political or governmental activity or function or responsibility." How incongruous that it should have been John F. Kennedy, our first Catholic president, who was the first to reverse this position and to place the previously withheld support of the United States behind the very modest United Nations program. In 1963, he stated at a press conference that research on human fertility and reproduction was of great importance, "a matter which we could certainly support." Congress, unfortunately, did not agree. The Senate Foreign Relations Committee included in the Foreign Aid Bill a provision for funds, "to conduct research into the problems of controlling population growth and to provide technical and other assistance. . . ." This section was eliminated in the final bill. It was axiomatic in the Senate for years that any consideration of birth control would be sandbagged by one or the other of a very small group of Catholic senators.

Lyndon Johnson, in 1965, was the first president to say flatly that the United States will "assist in family planning programs in nations which request such help." Congress, while now weakening somewhat on the subject, stated most explicitly for years that it would *not* allot money for the actual provision of contraceptives. It is enormously encouraging that the Agency for International Development (AID) planned to spend $35 million in "family planning" during fiscal 1968, a considerable improvement on the $4.2 million spent in the previous year, and that some of this money was to be spent on the distribution of contraceptives in countries requesting help. Hormonal pills in their present stage of development cost fifteen cents per woman per month wholesale (if you are paying $2.00 or more, someone is making money), let's say $1.50 per woman per year. If half of the AID money goes into the pockets of politicians, black-market operators, and legitimate administrators, this appropriation would benefit 12 million women—but this is only 1.7 percent of the estimated 700 million of childbearing age in the world. Still it is a beginning and a vastly greater one than that of any other agency, public or private. With IUD's (despite their weaknesses) we could do much more with the same money. Even in the United States, Congress now proposes to do something. The Social Security Act provided that something like $21 million be spent on family planning services in 1968. We thus join some twenty-three developing nations with family planning programs. If we could resist the insanities of wars and the arms race perhaps there would be hope. At the cost of the Vietnam war we could have the world ankle deep in pills. This is all, of course, provided that the Papal Encyclical will not eventually throw Congress back into the Dark Ages, a possibility that seems decreasingly likely.

If our national government has been slow to react, the attitude on the local political level has been antediluvian. Only in 1965 did the United States Supreme Court eliminate the remaining restrictions on birth control in several states—including a law in Connecticut that forbade medical doctors from advising their patients on birth control and individuals from using contraceptives. In Indiana the vending machines that adorn the walls of men's rooms in bars proclaim that the condoms are "sold only for the prevention of disease." Local wit apparently demands that the patrons scratch out the "dis." Abortion laws have been liberalized in five states (by 1969) and other changes are in the mill.

In summary, the Catholic attitude and position have been widely damaging. Even in countries where the individual family has not been unduly swayed by the prohibition against birth control, the official position *has*, with the result that the United Nations has so far been reduced to impotence in population control. In Latin America the church has without doubt been a considerable factor in producing the highest rate of human increase in the world. In many of these countries galloping population and abject poverty have proved a source of unceasing discontent and political ferment that has blocked progress in every direction— economic development, industrialization, self-sufficiency, education, adequate housing, and nutrition. In the United States, the stifling of research on contraception and the refusal to consider the population problem as a matter of public concern have, until 1968, prevented this country from taking a position of leadership or even from helping such countries as India that were all too eager for assistance.

There are those—not including me—who believe that the church position is totally self-serving; that it exists solely to produce more Catholics. Without denying the demonstrable fact that this idea has obviously entered the heads of some in the hierarchy, it must be pointed out that the ethical issue *is* agonizing to many honest people as things now stand. In the long run, however, the policy seems certain to be self-defeating even with respect to the ratio of Catholics to non-Catholics. The fact is that the proportion of Catholics in the world is decreasing; they are steadily approaching being swamped by the numbers of what my clerical ancestors quaintly called "the heathen." And, aside from the question of whether the church has the right to tell some 500 million Catholics how to manage procreation, I fail totally to see why it has the right to inflict its view on the non-Catholic 85 percent of the human race. Persuade, yes, dictate, no.

Social and Cultural Obstacles

FAR MORE SERIOUS than the Catholic interference with population control are various social and cultural factors. It is well recognized that the farmer the world over regards children as potential free farm hands. It is equally well known that as any society urbanizes, the birth rate tends to drop, presumably as the cost of store-bought groceries assumes a prominent place in the budget. I am personally intrigued with the idea that a considerable factor may be that there is just plain more to do in the city at night. From which flows my only semi-scurrilous notion that world-wide television and a good supply of horror movies and horse operas on the late show might do more to cure the world's population problems then ten years of sonorous debate at the United Nations. (Not that that is saying much.)

But the manifest utility of children in chopping cotton or planting rice is probably far less significant than the fact that in many areas of the world, offspring are engendered primarily to support one in his old age. There are societies like the classical Eskimo where things were so tough that the minute people got too old to carry their weight they were simply pushed out of the igloo. But far more frequently, even among people whom we consider quite backward, children support and respect their elders. This custom, both aspects of which we have now abandoned in the United States, has traditionally been an effective if primitive form of social security.

Nearly universal is the demonstration of virility to one's neighbors and rivals by the fathering of multitudinous offspring—particularly males. This point is so basic to the entire human race that it does not need dwelling on except to point out that the drive for fecundity is probably much more than cultural. It is probably genetically built into all creatures from cabbages to kings. There is no genetic reason to value longevity beyond the child-rearing age; every genetic reason to esteem procreation. Several billion years in the making, we cannot expect to abolish this drive by presidential fiat or even action of the Planned Parenthood Association. The desire to found a dynasty, to continue the family business, to extend one's philosophy and hence existence through children, will surely sustain the birth rate through such tribulations as the social emasculation of the American male. Bawdy houses, pool halls, and bars—not birth control clinics and PTA meetings—are the natural habitat of males. Rare is the male who fails to swell visibly with pride at the birth of a son. We seem totally unable to comprehend the fact that 99 percent of the 800 million Chinese were born one at a time, that some thirty-five years from now there will be, at the average world rate, 1.6 billion of them—more people than existed in the whole world at the turn of this century, and that thirty-five years later this single nation will contain as many people as *now* exist everywhere unless some control supervenes. Nonetheless, in the long run it seems obvious that the high-flown ethical, moral, and religious arguments against birth control and the basic sexual drives of the males of this world will succumb to the practicalities of birth and feeding as seen by the female. The impetus toward individual application of population control will come most strongly from the sex that rocks the cradle (which may soon be male).

Who, Me?

THIS RAISES THE POINT, however, that a very large part of the human race really regards population expansion as *good* not only for the ego, and family, but also for the business, or the community. There always seem to be local advantages to a little more, and surely some local situation is of absolutely no importance in the world problem. From the crude traditional view that another son was another farm hand, we have progressed to elegant rationalization, to take a local but typical example, that a thousand or two more students at a university provide leverage to increase the budget, hire more faculty, improve departments and facilities. Every year sees more pizza palaces, hamburger joints, filling stations, shopping centers, bars, and churches. The local Chamber of Commerce strives mightily to attract industry; we indulge in the most fulsome self-praise when we see a new payroll enter town, bringing a whole new group of employees, then complain bitterly that traffic is unbearable, parking impossible, school taxes insupportable. To question the desirability of further expansion is, apparently, totally heretical and un-American. Why, it seems almost like being opposed to motherhood.

Los Angeles crows mightily that it has passed Philadelphia and threatens Chicago as the second largest city. What matter that pollution is ruining the place and spreading steadily to more outlying areas, that freeways are becoming merely elongated parking lots where carbon monoxide concentration is barely below seriously toxic levels, that the famous orange groves have been chopped down to make room for ever more tasteless subdivisions? The Southwest is expanding to the bursting point with seemingly total disregard of the indisputable fact that the whole area depends on increasing mining of irreplaceable, vanishing fossil water. This onward and upward philosophy seems to permeate our every activity. I even have a distinct impression that we, as a nation, rather pout when we fail to set a new record for the number killed on a Fourth-of-July weekend. The radio and television announcers usually sound palpably disappointed.

There are leaders (not, discouragingly, the Pope) who talk about the desirability of slowing the expansion of the human race. They are few indeed and they speak with hedged caution. Virtually alone was Kingsley Davis with his flat and unassailable statement (in *Science*, 1967) that it is not enough, in the long run, to slow expansion of the human race; that eventually we must STOP it. We must stabilize our population at a number consistent with the capacity of the planet to support it, and, we may hope, to support it at a high, as contrasted with a bare subsistence-existence, level. We shall consider a bit later some of his suggestions, and strange indeed they sound to our American ears, attuned for nearly two centuries to full-throttled expansion of everything. The understanding of the necessity for control of population must begin with the proud father, the eager Brownie Troop, the ambitious merchant, the empire-building department head. In fact it must begin much farther back. It must begin with the individual elementary school child learning the meaning of exponential growth—the riddle of the newspaper folding to reach the sun and the fable of the bacteria swamping the solar system in three days.

Let George Do It

EVEN AMONG THOSE AWARE OF THE POPULATION PROBLEM, I think that a very basic difficulty, particularly in the most developed countries, is with the individual who assumes it is not his particular worry. Many interpretations have been placed on the horror story of the twenty-six people in New York City who were witnesses to the protracted beating to death of Mrs. Genovese, who heard her repeated screams for help, and who ignored them. Callousness —possibly, fear—yes, but I suspect that to a considerable degree it is simply that these people felt that it was not their business to get involved. I was really amazed a couple of weeks ago to see two young girls stop their car to remove a tree branch from the road after a violent local thunderstorm. It was not really blocking their way and obviously dozens of motorists had passed. I probably would have, had I not stopped for the girls. After all, there are people whose business it is to remove tree branches, prevent thugs from beating women, etc. We are all prone to this incredible compartmentalization. And surely someone must be coping with the population problem over in India or wherever it is a nuisance.

The incredible thing is the lack of intercommunication. Each group knows that it has problems and will have bigger ones, but no one seems to pay attention to the other guy, or to the sum total. If one reads the general scientific literature with this sort of question in mind, it becomes quickly apparent that in area after area experts are screaming their heads off. *Science* magazine is intended for the general scientific audience. Over the past few years it has had article after article expressing real concern over the future with regard to air and water pollution, water shortages, food shortages, mineral shortages, etc. So have *The Sciences, Science News, American Scientist,* and *Scientific American.* No one argues with the data or conclusions, yet I find, for example, essentially no bacteriologists concerned with the seriousness of biological pollution and the possibility of epidemic disease in an ever more crowded society. These problems are deemed worthy of the attentions of only a few rather old-fashioned and dull people, it seems. And I know, personally, only one botanist who is enough worried about the limitations of food production to work on the problem.

Here at Indiana University we have a group of faculty concerned with population problems. We recently sponsored a national meeting concerned with important global aspects of the question. Yet for years whenever I have pointed out that our own campus is becoming a madhouse and that our own power plant is the most serious single contributor of local atmospheric pollution and that we should do something, I have found that everyone thought I was making a joke. Hundreds of acres of surrounding farmland have been swallowed up by the expanding community; nearly 11,000 acres, largely of good farming bottomland, have been engulfed to create a new reservoir that is the largest lake in the state. Our newest dormitories are two miles from the farthest class room with no satisfactory·public transportation. Students use cars, largely against regulations, to get to classes. The traffic around campus is often a total mess, parking is impossible, frequently a haze of exhaust fumes hangs in the streets. And not one single person seems to feel the slightest need to be personally concerned about the long-term effects or eventual limits of all of this admittedly very local problem. Local, but multiplied by the thousands all over the United States alone. Everyone is too busy coping with his own little concerns. I have not found a single local businessman who regards the expansion of Bloomington, Indiana, as anything but splendid.

When I talk about the *world* population problem, I find people very concerned indeed. In giving nearly 100 lectures and television presentations, I have never failed to find the audience really alarmed at the picture I present. Everyone feels very strongly that something must be done. And fast. No one has ever discussed the local situation about which one might assume we *could* do something. Only two people have ever asked me what *they* could or should do. But everyone agrees that it's bad. Someone better be doing something about it. Someone else.

Communication

To be good is noble. To tell others how
to be good is much nobler—and no trouble.
—*Attributed to* MARK TWAIN

WE ALL REALIZE THAT COMMUNICATION IS A TWO-WAY street, that it is not enough to talk, someone has to listen; that there exists a sort of Newton's law of communication—"For every action there must be an equal and opposite reaction"—if the communication is to be effective. But because there are so many millions of local problems of human society, we desperately need synthesis in addition to listening. It is all too easy to lose sight of the fact that a very large proportion of our difficulties have to do with the Siamese twins of human population and increasing per capita material demands.

The question is how to make the maximum number of people aware of these facts. And this brings up what may be the most important point of all. We are confronted with a difficulty that is intuitively obvious but seldom specifically discussed. We speak constantly of the "information explosion" as we do of the "population explosion" and fail to realize that neither is mysterious but both are governed by universal and elementary laws of biology and communication. By now I hope that we can all agree that there is nothing mysterious or inexplicable about the population explosion. But as my colleague Richard B. Curtis first pointed out to me, the problem of information exchange was equally inevitable given the population problem. The main point is so fundamental that it deserves to be stressed:

The number of links of communication among individuals increases essentially as an exponential of the number of individuals; but with humans the increase of THIS *number is already an exponential.*

We see another area of human society, then, in which the basic exponential of population increase is compounded by an increase per capita, as it were, but in this case, unlike those involving material demands for metals and water, the exponential is compounded as another exponential—$N^{(x)^y}$, in essence.

Since this is complicated, even mathematically, we might consider examples with very small numbers. If two people meet to discuss a problem, there is a single link of communication. If three people meet, each can speak with two others, giving three links. With four people the number of pairs goes up to six, with five people to ten. But we have considered only links between pairs of people. With larger groups many other possibilities exist. The top boss may wish to speak with his entire office force individually, giving n-links of communication, but he may also wish to address them all simultaneously on the glories of honest endeavor. This is another link. He may also elect to speak to half the group, say the executives, and then the other half, say the secretaries, about the washroom problem. If he is concerned with promotion of individuals, he might want to talk simultaneously to the entire group excluding a single individual, but in all possible combinations, etc. Obviously when even five or six people are involved, the situation becomes very complex and the number of channels of communication mounts very rapidly. If you have the feeling, as I often do, that you spend all of your time in meetings, you now understand why. The amount of time spent in communicating a viewpoint to various groups, getting back opinions, coordinating them, accommodating them, and achieving a unified effort becomes appalling. This would be true even if everyone restricted his attention to the issue at stake (I should live so long!) and acted unemotionally and in good faith.

To return to the population problem, we all know that we have staggering problems in achieving mutual understanding. The barriers of distance, of a multiplicity of languages, of illiteracy, of lack of adequate means of communication are obvious to us all. And we all understand that there are basic differences in attitude between, for instance, the Japanese, who suffer from severe over-crowding, and the Australians, who have seemingly vast expanses of land to be developed. We have seen the difficulties in reaching a practical solution to such a seemingly simple, but actually very complex, problem as accommodating the food surpluses of the United States to the semistarvation of the Indians and Africans. Scientists are often tongue-tied (or loquaciously ineffective) in discussing with non-scientists, such as United States Congressmen, such technically complicated questions as why we need to have more time and to invest more money in study of basic problems of radiation damage before we can give firm, reliable figures on permissable fall-out or increases in environmental radiation background from nuclear power plants. Why must we go to such enormous expense to dispose of radioactive waste? One must either take the answer on faith or spend a lot of time learning basic facts and principles in several areas of science.

In considering anything as complicated as birth control, involving not only obvious self-interest but all sorts of ramifications of ethics, religion, culture, cost, and logistics, the problem of communication seems to me perhaps the most basic one. And the most fundamental fact of all is that with 3.5 billion people the sheer number of links of communication possible is overwhelming. A solution is obviously hopeless without the most careful organization, yet of the hundreds of nations involved, a number of the most important are not even on speaking terms.

8. / Birth, Population, and Death

As a trivial beginning, I often think that perhaps we can establish communication at the individual level by a very simple and available device, the transistor radio. Even now, it is frequently reported that one finds them in the darkest and most primitive recesses of human occupancy. If they were made very cheap and reliable and then distributed universally not as a propaganda weapon but as a source of entertainment, at least we would have the potentiality for basic communication. And then surely Madison Avenue could slip in the word about the advantages of birth control and the popularity with the younger set of the vasectomized male and make it all seem desirable. But I am afraid that to many this approach will sound hopelessly naive. We tend to consider any important issue, unfortunately, first at the lofty intellectual level with discussions of rights and principles, and then, if that is not enough to destroy the topic, to stiletto it to death by diplomacy.

Education and Acceptance in Developing Societies

It has often been said—with what justification I do not know—that anthropologists have found tribes so primitive that they did not know that sexual intercourse produced babies but never tribes lacking the knowledge to make fermented alcoholic beverages. I would image that such tribes, nowadays, are hard to find. But knowing where babies come from, the next question is whether people *want* to do something about it. It does not take a very advanced intellegence to see the undesirability of bringing into the world children who will starve or at best place an intolerable burden on the family. As we have commented before, women who have already borne several children are usually eager, apparently the world over, to receive information and to participate in a birth control program. For them social and religious strictures against birth control seem to be relatively unimportant. In a number of pilot efforts to establish use of the pill or IUD or

211

condom, in addition to the problems of early acceptance, there are those of communicating technique and logistics. And here one sees communication reduced to its essence—how to reach isolated people who lack access to the usual media. It has been repeatedly pointed out that in India the slow progress of the governmentally sponsored family planning program has been attributable to very basic factors. The 500 million people speak 800 languages and dialects; illiteracy is very high; they lack almost completely access to newspapers, magazines, radio, television, or even regular mail.

Incredibly I have seen the same sort of difficulty at what we would like to regard as the other end of the scale—American urban society. We also have our underdeveloped social strata, and the Planned Parenthood organization in my city finds that the great difficulty is not in persuading couples with several children to use contraceptives, it is in reaching them early and effectively. The people best able to afford children really need only to be made aware of the necessity for population control. Since they are the reading and discussing public, this should be fairly easy. They will, then, presumably limit their families without needing Planned Parenthood. Unfortunately, those least able to afford children do not avail themselves of the service. Newspaper publicity has been quite ineffective as a means of persuasion, and the use of spot announcements on the radio equally so. A local television program featured Planned Parenthood weekly over a period of months at a time when available information would suggest that the listeners were exactly the women the group was trying to reach. It was emphasized constantly that no one would be forced to do anything, that no fee would be charged unless the family could afford it, and that the patient could choose a technique consistent with his religion or preferences. Not one single patient is known to have come to the clinic as a result. The most effective inducement seems to be the most inefficient and costly—having social workers discuss the matters with families on relief or involved in other difficulties. This is not a matter of coercion; it is partly a question of removing concern over going to the clinic but also of overcoming simple inertia. Most of these women are anxious, at the level of rational consciousness, to avoid further children, but, to put it bluntly, they almost literally, and often quite literally, require to be taken by the hand and led to the clinic. This reluctance has been so striking that it seems obvious that more is involved than poverty and ignorance. Of course, higher welfare payments often result from larger families. But in working with them, my wife and her colleagues at Planned Parenthood have been repeatedly and increasingly impressed with the degree to which having a baby is an event of tremendous importance in the otherwise dull and monotonous lives of welfare-level women. It is exciting, highly approved socially among their friends, and traditional. Also the hospital stay amounts to a beautiful three- or four-day vacation—unsually, today, at the expense of Blue Cross or a social agency. Then one brings home a baby to be admired, played with, and fussed over for months. Incredible and naive as it may seem, persuasion of people at this level to have fewer children may very easily involve providing them with a substitute form of gratification.

In undeveloped countries there are other problems. The birth control methodology used routinely in the highly developed, urbanized countries often turns out to be difficult or impossible in the wilds of Africa, for example. Problems of supply can be overcome, materials can be provided free, but such elementary necessities as that for hot water, a little privacy, and an understanding of the calendar often prove limiting. In one study the contraceptive pill was provided free and the women given a string of beads. Each day a bead was to be moved and the pills taken on days with white beads, not on days with black beads. Many women proved incapable of managing even this stratagem. But a less anticipated difficulty arose from the belief that magic was involved. Convinced that it lay in the beads, the men not infrequently understood just enough to diddle them in the furtherance of conjugal felicity. (A newer, simpler technique is to package the pills seriatim, twenty hormonal followed by eight vitamin pills.)

I think that if any conclusion can be drawn it is that in the underdeveloped world, if not everywhere, there are certainly the anticipated problems that may be described as communication, education, propaganda, or brain-washing as suits your temperament. It has also become obvious that we need methods of birth control that are very inexpensive and so simple that they require a minimum of technical training for introduction and little or no training or attention for regular use. They will have to be different in these regards from the techniques that have been so successful in Europe, the United States, and Japan. But most of all, we can see that the primary goal must be to reach fecund couples earlier; to persuade them that human society and, specifically, *they* do not need and cannot *afford* more than the replacement number of children. And I am convinced that here the question is not only one of talking but listening. We do not yet adequately understand the motivations of the people in the ghettoes of this country toward larger families, we need to know much more about why people all over the world feel they want or need more children. It seems unlikely that we can really persuade on the rational or intellectual level; the drives are much more basic.

METHODS OF BIRTH CONTROL

HAVING REACHED PEOPLE and persuaded them, we are then confronted with the problem of techniques.

There is, of course, nothing new about birth control. As with the TV viewers who claim to watch only the symphony and ballet, but who are usually discovered watching soap operas and pro football, the only new thing is admitting that birth control exists and is a discussable phenomenon. Abortion and infanticide (especially of females) were known at the dawn of history. Discussions of *coitus interruptus* (premature withdrawal) are equally ancient. Continence, through the ages, has been regularly and highly recommended by the clergy—especially the elderly or celibate clergy. The condom, interestingly, also turns out to be a rather ancient device, used as early as the sixteenth century. Practical contraception, however, probably dates from about 1880 with the introduction of the diaphragm, especially with the later improvement of spermacidal jelly. This is interesting because the effectiveness of diaphragm-jelly (twelve pregnancies per 100 women per year) is not appreciably greater than that of the long-available condom (at fourteen). Its greater success is therefore almost surely attributable mostly to the greater interest of the female in the avoidance of pregnancy.

The Pill

THE GREAT LEAP FORWARD came with the development of the hormonal contraceptive pill, whose use in the United States began in the 1950's. One might note, however, that the birth rate in this country took a sharp turn downward several years before the introduction of this most effective (0.3 pregnancies per 100 women per year) technique. Although the pill has been an important step, we should note a number of weaknesses in its use as a world-wide panacea for population control. In its present form the method is too expensive for universal use in underdeveloped countries. There are, moreover, some reservations about its use continuously during the entire childbearing life of a woman. Side effects (for example, excessive blood clotting) are rare (with three fatalities per 100,000 women) but exist. Despite the alarm expressed recently in hearings in the United States Congress— with much publicity—the sober evaluation of the majority of authorities is that the pill is generally safe. As pointed out again and again, the risks of childbearing are certainly greater, and, with proper medical supervision, even the rare side reactions are avoidable. No one can exclude beyond conceivability the chance that the hormones of present contraceptive pills *may* eventually increase the likelihood of cancer, but most authorities consider the risk very small. Unfortunately because of the nature of cancer only time will settle this question. But it must be reemphasized that all of these possibilities are marginal, and much research is now being devoted toward the development of hormonal pills that will avoid even these slight potential risks.

The difficulty with the pill as a method of population control is not the medical risk but the seemingly trivial one that women, even educated, well-motivated women, find it difficult to remember absolute unfailing adherence to the necessary regimen. With some of the pills in current use, skipping one day can result in pregnancy; with the best now available, skipping two days is risky. The proponents of the pill are convinced that the small percentage of failures is due to forgetfulness, not inadequacy of the hormones. In primitive areas, of course, the cost of even the low dosage pills and the logistics of supplying the women are strong deterrents.

The IUD

A MOST PROMISING SOLUTION TO THESE PROBLEMS was the intrauterine device (IUD). Although the basic idea dates from the 1920's, plastic "loops" made the technique practical only in 1959. In theory the device, which takes a number of forms, is inserted aseptically in the uterus and stays there preventing conception until removed. Insertion and removal require trained technicians or doctors but can be accomplished quickly and simply. The beauty of the method, in theory, is that a woman can use the loop as long as desired and then restore her fertility at will. Unfortunately widespread use has revealed a number of discouraging drawbacks. Reaching women in primitive areas with the necessary skilled technicians is difficult. As we have seen, most women accept the IUD only after they have had several children. But more serious is the fact that a considerable proportion of women either reject the loop spontaneously, are troubled with persistent bleeding, or find it uncomfortable and have it removed. In the United States even with the best loop the removal rate has been 30 percent in four years; in Taiwan the rate was 50 percent in two. The efficacy (five pregnancies per 100 women per year) is not as high as that of the pill and although they are rare, quite serious side reactions (perforations of the uterus, for example) have been reported. Many doctors are uneasy because the mode of operation of the IUD is not really understood. Its chief function seems to be as an irritant, and this raises the possibility—assumedly remote—or increased incidence of uterine cancer as a long-term result. There is now considerably less enthusiasm for this device than a few years ago when it seemed a means to salvation. Nonetheless the IUD *is* in use by millions and *is* preventing unwanted births in huge numbers all over the world. Improvements in design may obviate the present difficulties.

Sterilization

Judge, O you gods. . . . This was the most unkindest cut of all.
—Shakespeare, *Julius Caesar*

THE INDIAN GOVERNMENT is currently trying a mass campaign of male sterilization through the tying or severing (vasectomy) of the tubes from the testicles through which the sperm are released. This method is sure (.003 pregnancies per 100 women per year) and permanent, and the operation is simple. In the United States, where the average male apparently has a totally superstitious fear that his manhood will be infringed by vasectomy, it has met with very little acceptance. Many hospitals, because of Catholic control or influence, will not allow the operation. These objections are not found in India, but even with the present program of bribery it does not seem possible that they can perform enough operations to achieve the desired result. The current scheme involves the posting in railway stations, etc. of professional procurers who receive ten rupees ($1.33) for each person brought in for the operation. The sterilizee receives twenty rupees if a man, fifteen if a woman. The surgeon gets six per vasectomy, ten per tubectomy (for women), and his assistant three. The five rupees-worth of medicine used brings the total cost to about six dollars per sterilization.

But even with this program, the difficulties have been great. We have noted that the average man vasectomized has already fathered 4.5 children. And even though India has congratulated itself heartily on 6 million sterilizations (between 1956 and 1969), we must remember that the population is now 500 million, with 90 million couples in the childbearing age group. With something like 5 million men entering the breeding pool per year, even the 1.4 million sterilizations (both men and women) in the peak year of 1967 are obviously inadequate as a sole means of control. Condoms, however, are also provided free at 20,000 health stations and sold for two cents per package of three at tobacconists, grocery stores, etc. Although no one is sure about the eventual effectiveness of this program, the progress has been sufficient to incite a vigorous protest by the organized eunuchs of the state of Uttar Pradash. A leader, Dilban Khwaja, has said, "We cannot tolerate it. Singing and dancing to mark the birth of boy babies is our main source of income. We have launched our campaign against family planning to protect our very existence."

As a general solution, it must be noted that the main disadvantage (or advantage) of sterilization is that the process is irreversible, in the large majority of cases. A local Planned Parenthood physician also reports that it seems, strangely, not to be 100 percent efficient; he is casting a suspicious eye at milkmen and TV repairmen.

Abortion

IT IS A SAD COMMENTARY on the present state of the art of birth control that contraception has been really effective—if one is to talk in terms of actual national birth rate—only when backed up by abortion. A dramatic example is Japan, where use (mainly) of the rather inefficient condom plus legalized, inexpensive abortion has been responsible for cutting the birth rate by more than half, from a disastrous thirty-four to less than fourteen per year per 1000 inhabitants. It is an even sadder, if wry, commentary that population pressure alone did not accomplish this salutary result. During the American occupation, a major problem (but at the same time an aid to the economy) was prostitution. There is considerable reason to believe that the prospect of innumerable half-American children was the clincher in securing legalized abortion. We might note that the legislation responsible (1948) was called not a population-control act, but a Eugenics Protection Act. So much for our smug occidental superiority. Also widely used in the European Communist countries, abortion has proved a powerful corrective. In the Argentine it is claimed that there is one (illegal) abortion per live birth. In Uruguay the illegal abortion rate is said to exceed the birth rate three to one. Although it is quite safe and simple, when done under proper medical circumstances, there is widespread opinion in the United States, at least, that abortion is little short of murder. In a country where the necessity was as great as in Japan, public opinion seems to have been able to accept this Draconian solution to the population problem. I think that we can hope with considerable justification, however, that equally effective and less drastic methods are within our grasp.

New Techniques

I ALWAYS FIND IT SOMEWHAT OBJECTIONABLE to write of scientific pie in the sky, but it is only reasonable to point out that a number of new techniques for birth control seem to be in promising stages of development. The "morning after" pill seems useful and promising for the absent-minded or casually promiscuous. The mini-pill of progestin—a hormone but with different action from that of the present estrogen pill— promises to reduce dosages and expense greatly and to offer the advantage that one need not count nor juggle beads since the pill is taken daily. So far, however, the method is somewhat less efficacious. An even more interesting possibility is that of surgical implants of a pellet of progestin hormone. The technique works in rats, with a single implant sufficing for the animal's life. The hope is that an operation no more complex than a hypodermic shot will turn out to leave the human female infertile for years or perhaps for as long as she wishes. If she changes her mind it will be equally simple to remove the implant. Present plans of the Population Council set 1972 as the date when the technique may be ready for mass use. There have been several suggestions for male contraceptive pills, but, as we have already commented, it is still the female who bears the child and proves more reliably motivated to birth control. And even more discouraging is the fact that the only male pill devised so far produces an aversion to alcohol. After all, why take birth control pills if you ain't gonna celebrate?

These, admittedly, are hoped-for developments, but a number of possibilities exist. The difficulty is that we are beginning large-scale research in this area rather late. The present experiments should have been done a couple of decades ago and quite possibly would have been were it not for the alleged unwillingness of the American people—the most research-minded people on earth—to countenance the investigation of the biology of human fertility. It is perhaps not inappropriate to point out that a great pioneer in this area was eased out of one of our most prestigious universities in the 1930's just because he proposed to study exactly these "indelicate" problems, the solutions to which are now so urgently needed.

NATIONAL PROGRAMS

GIVEN THE MEANS FOR EFFECTIVE BIRTH CONTROL, many authorities automatically think of the next logical step as state, national, or world bureaucratic dictation. Is there an alternative to eventual world-wide planning and legal restrictions to *force* the stabilization of the human race? As I have commented already, the likelihood of agreement on this subject seems at the moment remote. It may be that we shall never need it, that voluntary action by individuals, with the support of state or national organizations, will be adequate. There is evidence that such a program might succeed too well here and there. We have already noted the almost unbelievable reduction of the Japanese birth rate in twenty years. Some Japanese leaders now fear that a shortage of people of working age may result. If the objective of such national planning is to be zero growth of the population the birth rate must be balanced with the death rate. With a crude birth rate of 13.7 per 1000 and a death rate of 6.8 Japan is still far from balance, but the annual growth rate is below 1 percent and the birth rate is still dropping. For contrast one might look at Venezuela, where the corresponding figures of forty-seven births and ten deaths leave a net growth rate of 3.7 percent or a doubling time of less than twenty years.

Family Planning

FAMILY PLANNING is being actively advocated in some twenty-three countries. In Taiwan, of the women in the child-bearing age group something like one in four to six have been equipped with IUD's. Korea has well over 2000 workers in the field supplying contraceptive materials (largely IUD's) and actively propagandizing. But, as Kingsley Davis points out, the figures excluded those women who still want children, and the programs so far are aimed only at discouragingly modest reductions in the birth rate. He comments further: "The Pakistan plan, adopted in 1966, aims to reduce the birth rate from 50 to 40 per thousand (!) by 1970; the Indian plan aims to reduce the rate from 40 to 25 'as soon as possible'; and the Korean aim is to cut population growth from 2.9 to 1.2 percent by 1980." None of these plans could conceivably be considered as aimed at the controlled population desperately needed in these overcrowded countries. To accomplish this objective—which no one at the governmental policy level seems to regard as *the* objective—requires balancing birth and immigration rates with deaths and emigrations. It is not at all inconceivable that a country without an overall program, instead of one aimed only at "family planning" or "fertility reduction," could find itself tending toward a considerable imbalance—possibly even in the direction of a net loss of population, though I do not think we have to worry about this yet.

Davis concludes that the best one can say about all of the national planning programs now extant is that they are starts in the right direction, interim plans to accustom people to the idea of population management. He feels strongly that we must face the facts and insist on total national control with the objective of stabilization, not haphazard family planning leaving the eventual outcome to chance. "Reliance on family planning allows people to feel that 'something is being done about the population problem' without the need for painful social changes."

Examination of the other side of the population coin, the countries with the highest rates of increase, seems at first to confirm the value of family planning. In all of these areas there either has been no national program or there is one so lately established as to have had as yet no effect. Davis notes, however, that social forces are at work that may be more important than, and may be largely responsible for, the population policies. In most areas where they seem effective, there has been a strong trend toward urbanization and industrialization (as in Taiwan and Japan), which always results in rapidly dropping birth rates. Thus the countries with strong programs have industrial-urban rather than peasant-agrarian societies. The areas without population programs are just those in which the social structure tends to support large families and those in which there are classic obstacles to birth control—lack of general education, inadequate communications, inbred conservatism, Catholicism. In other words the population policies may simply be a means of providing formally the information and means toward an end already decided on by the individual because of social pressures.

Davis considers it unproved that family planning can be a success as a national program imposed from above on an oppositely motivated or indifferent society. He obviously thinks that the first step must be the natural or deliberate creation of pressures that will impel the individual couple toward birth control. Then and only then, he believes, a national policy of family planning can be a great help in producing a significant drop in the birth rate. But it is only a help. "To continue to offer a remedy as a cure long after it has been shown merely to ameliorate the disease is either quackery or wishful thinking." His fear is that reliance on family planning is merely avoidance of the real question—that of how populations are to be stabilized.

Programs for the Future

INSTEAD KINGSLEY DAVIS purposes a frontal attack on the real problem of stabilization. His ideas are, I think, quite clearly unacceptable at present, so radical that they will take a lot of getting used to. He proposes to deemphasize family size by keeping present controls over illegitimate childbirth while making the most of factors that lead people to avoid or postpone marriage and by instituting conditions that will motivate those who marry to keep their families small.

Noting that "the 'baby boom' is usually associated with a return to younger marriages," he suggests that we can lower the birth rate quite appreciably by discouraging them. He regards legal restrictions as probably ineffective and certainly repugnant in our present social structure. But decisions about the proper time for marriage, the raising of a family, and the size of a family have traditionally been made as a result of social and economic conditions. In various nations at various times the average marrying age has varied considerably, depending on such factors as "housing shortages, unemployment, the requirement for overseas military service, high costs of education, and the inadequacy of consumer services." We could, Davis thinks, manipulate the situation deliberately, by allowing "economic advantages to accrue to the single as opposed to the married individual, and to the small as opposed to the large family."

The government could pay people to permit themselves to be sterilized; all costs of abortion could be paid by the government; a substantial fee could be charged for a marriage license; a 'child tax' could be levied; there could be a requirement that illegitimate pregnancies be aborted.... [Governments] could cease taxing single people more than married ones; stop giving parents special tax exemptions; .. stop awarding public housing on the basis of family size; stop granting fellowships and other educational aids ... to married students; cease outlawing abortions and sterilizations; and relax rules that allow the use of harmless contraceptives only with medical permission.

He also feels that we could reduce the drive of both men and women toward family life by such stratagems as requiring or at least impelling women to work outside the home. "If social life were organized around the place of work rather than around the home or neighborhood, many women would develop interests that would compete with family interests. Approximately this policy is now followed in several Communist countries, and even the less developed of these currently have extremely low birth rates."

The measures that would be required to implement such a goal, though not so revolutionary as a Brave New World or a Communist Utopia, nevertheless tend to offend most people reared in existing societies. As a consequence, the goal of so-called population control is implicit and vague; the method is only family planning. This method, far from de-emphasizing the family, is familistic. . . . The things that make family planning acceptable are the very things that make it ineffective for population control. By stressing the right of parents to have the number of children they want, it evades the basic question of population policy, which is how to give societies the number of children they need.

In countries where contraception is used, a realistic proposal of lowering the birth rate reads like a catalogue of horrors: squeeze consumers through taxation and inflation; make housing very scarce by limiting construction; force wives and mothers to work outside the home to offset the inadequacy of male wages, yet provide few child care facilities. . . . No government will institute such hardships simply for the purpose of controlling growth.

The conclusion, then, is that family planning is useful and that contraception offers us the techniques for the control of population but that "such programs must be supplemented with equal or greater investments in research and experimentation to determine the. . . . socioeconomic measures" required for solution of the world's population problems.

Although Davis's proposals sound in many ways appalling, we must recognize that the alternatives presented by continued population growth are even more so. We must certainly reverse the trend of rewarding large families on the implicit ground (justifiable until quite recently) that more people are needed for the nation, that there are worlds yet to conquer, frontiers to be colonized. I would like to think that by education based on understanding of the motivations of potential parents we can stop short of some of the repressive measures suggested in the "catalogue of horrors" or even short of the centralized manipulation that always seems so appealing to social reformers.

Love Marriage

IT SEEMS QUITE OBVIOUS that even now or certainly in the very near future we can make childbearing a completely voluntary step. As contraception improves and as acceptance is attained, there exists the possibility, long suggested and put forth again recently by anthropologist Margaret Mead, of creating two kinds of marriages. Young people who are in love could live together legally simply by registering at city hall. Explicit in the relationship would be the use of completely effective contraception, possibly backed by legal abortion. The marriage could be rescinded simply by returning to city hall and having it crossed off the books. When a couple decided that theirs was a stable relationship or when they met certain requirements, possibly the attainment of a particular legal age, they could enter into the second type of marriage, with more formality, and could then have children. The break-up of marriage with children could then be taken even more seriously, possibly, than divorce today.

I am sure a large proportion of present-day Americans will automatically recoil with unbelieving horror at such a "grossly immoral" suggestion. I am personally convinced that such an attitude is unrealistic and illogical, and that we *must* confront the arguments that favor some such solution. In the first place, I hope that we can face the fact that the population problem is right now at the point where drastic measures are in order. Social upheaval is going to occur whether we like it or not and that right soon. So here are the arguments as I see them in the writing of Margaret Mead and others:

It must be obvious that whether we like it or not, love relationships are presently in existence in untold numbers. Lacking adequate contraception, the result in the United States is that in one marriage in six (a commonly accepted figure) the bride is pregnant. The girl who has to leave high school to bear an illegitimate baby is so commonplace as to be scarcely scandalous. That this is severely traumatic to the couple and their families is beyond question. That illegal abortion—the usual "first thought" alternative—is probably more traumatic both physically and psychologically is not questioned by any doctor to whom I have talked. But the forced marriage between youngsters in their first infatuation is guaranteed to place virtually insurmountable obstacles in front of a relationship that requires everything favorable going for it. Almost no adult doubts that the choice of a life partner at high school age is totally undesirable. Of such stuff is our divorce rate of over one per four marriages made. That divorce is bad enough, but far worse when children are involved, is attested to not only by common knowledge but even more strongly by statistics on delinquency, school dropouts, youthful crime, ghetto rioting, and even drug addiction. Unfortunately one cannot measure in any such objective way the sum of human misery from bad marriages kept in force by social or religious pressure.

In universities the country over, couples are living together. In many instances the administration, feeling forced by the uncontrollable facts plus pressure from student organizations, has had to accept this situation in one way or another. We are currently seeing nationally a struggle of university administrations vs. parents and trustees, who often think that the university in accepting their children and money is obligated to stand *in loco parentis*, maintaining moral and behavioral standards that the parents themselves were often unwilling or unable to enforce. It is a curious commentary that the local campus police estimate that at least 85 percent of disciplinary and particularly moral problems arise because of the automobiles with which parents equip their children and which parents insist on their having available at the university.

The long and short of it is that our present social structure is more and more opposed to basic biological facts. The human is capable of procreation at something like age thirteen, but the education and training required by our society forces an average delay in marriage of nearly ten years. This situation is being exacerbated by the steadily increasing proportion of our population that completes a college degree. The median age at marriage is now about twenty-two years, the median duration of marriages a little over seven years.

Many people are worried that the availability of contraceptives "will lead to a tremendous general decline in morals." This attitude seems to me largely a case of our having become trapped in our own definitions. When we see a young unmarried couple walking around holding hands, we may make a mental note that public display of affection is in somewhat questionable taste, but no one is seriously concerned. The good night kiss at the family (or sorority) door is certainly a part of life from junior high school up even though some would deprecate the custom. But when a couple is caught in fornication, then we can all agree that the act is immoral, and we are apt, if parental to one of the pair, to be pretty upset. The difference is quite simply that handholding does not bring babies, fornication does.

We understand very well that a baby born to an unmarried young couple creates a socially most undesirable situation with widespreading ramifications, none of them good. We know that even if the couple gets married to avoid some of the problems, others are created. They may not really like each other that much, especially in the long run; they may not be ready to be tied down; they may not have the education or training to support a family; they may resent not only each other and the parents or society that forced them into the marriage, but, worst of all, the baby. To avoid all of these complications we place on our young very strong moral—and even legal—strictures to avoid the problem in the first place.

But suppose that sexual intercourse involved no risk whatsoever of having a baby. The socially undesirable potential complications no longer exist. So why is this immoral? It seems a little ridiculous to say that it is still immoral because they have not obtained a license and had a few words muttered over them by a bored city clerk. If that will make you happy, nothing is simpler to arrange. Most of the complications of divorce arise because of children. If there are none, why not face the fact and make divorce as simple as the original marriage? Of course there may be property rights involved. But surely that is not where the immorality lies. If these are young people marrying not for property rights but for love and if there is no property anyway, where are the complications? Only in the minds of lawyers anxious for divorce fees, I am afraid. It costs $2 to get married, a minimum of $150 for a divorce.

To me Margaret Mead's proposal of baby-less trial marriages must be taken seriously and discussed. It would establish one of Kingsley Davis's main proposals for the reduction of the birth rate—older marriage (so far as children are concerned). It would avoid a very large number of the disadvantages of present-day unsuccessful marriages and broken homes with children. It is sure that if we are driven to control of the population by other much more stringent means, we shall have to swallow a great many far more disagreeable social consequences.

THE TRAP

THE BIRTH RATE VARIES ENORMOUSLY in various parts of the world, as we have already seen. The sex and age adjusted average rate in underdeveloped areas currently stands at forty to forty-five per 1000 per year, while the rate in Europe is about nineteen and in North America about twenty-seven per 1000. The areas of highest rate are Latin America with forty-two, southern Asia with forty-five, and Africa with forty-nine per 1000. In view of these facts, it is altogether tempting to congratulate ourselves that in the United States and other developed countries we have made a good beginning. Our crude birth rate* has fallen from a high of twenty-five in 1955 to a current (and still dropping) figure of about nineteen per 1000.

The rate in Japan has dropped from a high of thirty-four to a present value of fourteen. Comparable to the general European rate of nineteen, the U.S.S.R. has twenty. All of this would seem to show what can be done and to be most encouraging.

The hooker, of course, is that the sharp drops have occurred in the most highly developed countries, where communication, levels of education, urbanization, and, in some instances, severe crowding have all combined to produce quick results. We have contrasted these situations with India, for example, where the communication is abysmal, motivation poor, trained medical technicians in hopelessly short supply, etc. And it is exactly in these latter areas that the population is now so high that starvation is an almost immediate threat. It is quite obvious that to avoid rather imminent famine drastic steps will be necessary, yet progress in India has been snail-like despite an intensive government program of population control.

Unless a balance can be attained within a very few years, moreover, we will confront a potentially even more disastrous situation—mushrooming population of the underdeveloped areas demanding enormous technical assistance of every kind and an increasing shortage of trained people to fill the needs. Where will Asia and Africa find the agricultural experts, teachers, electronic engineers, plant geneticists, fertilizer chemists, water and sewage

*The crude birth rate is based on total population and hence is lower than the adjusted rate based on the numbers of those of childbearing age.

bacteriologists, doctors, dentists, metallurgical engineers. . . ?
In the long run they must train their own, but it is obvious that
for a considerable length of time they will depend on the developed countries to provide actual help and to train indigenous
specialists. I feel personally that present trends in the developed
countries could set up a technical imbalance all too quickly. If
we reduced our United States growth rate to zero, the effect on
the world population would be almost trivial, since we constitute
only 0.2 billion out of a total population of about 3.5 billion—
less that 6 percent. But the drop in the total production of the
technically trained would be little short of disastrous. The world
is indeed too much with us, we can no longer tolerate unilateral
decisions in the population area. My own conclusion is that we
must set an example of a steadily dropping birth rate to convince
the underdeveloped countries that our own motives are not political, but that it is most important to develop a world-wide program.

SUMMARY

THAT THE HUMAN RACE MUST CONTROL its present
headlong expansion cannot be doubted. In far too many areas
serious troubles (notably famines) threaten even in the short run,
in the long run it is inescapable that we must bring the rate of
net expansion to zero, let us hope at a point where the race can
live at a high standard within the resources of the planet. The
technology for population control is available now, though its
world-wide application would be expensive and difficult. There
seems no reason to doubt that simpler, less expensive techniques
can be developed to replace present methods, which are based on
a very few years of active research on a small scale. But it seems
abundantly clear that the time is all too short in which we must
mount a vigorous world-wide, strongly supported program of

population limitation. There is no question that we *can* do it, only whether we will. That the Catholic church is a considerable obstacle cannot be denied, but its role is more that of obstructing official action and support in the developed countries than of contributing to actual numbers of the total world population. The major problems are clearly education, the overcoming of cultural obstacles, the provision of adequate official support, and, perhaps most of all, communication at the level of the basic motivations involved.

Epilogue

IN THE ARRAY OF PROBLEMS that confronts the human race and presages future trouble, there are two constantly recurring basic factors—the exponential growth of population and the increase in per capita consumption of many resources. In attacking the onslaught of pollution, food and water inadequacies, mineral shortages, etc., it is of paramount importance to keep constantly in mind that these *are* the basic factors and to avoid being led continuously into emergency Band-Aid and boat-bailing remedies while neglecting the fundamental causes.

With the human population, as with that of any other organism, there is a limit to the number of individuals supportable within the environment. We do not know that number with respect to any factor that affects us, but it exists. No species can grow exponentially for an indefinite period no matter how slow the rate of doubling. The human has compounded the problem by increasing in numbers at an ever faster rate. The present average doubling time of thirty-five years is intolerable, the twenty- to twenty-five-year rates of a number of countries are catastrophic.

The regulation of biological populations requires a balancing of birth and death rates. Usually, control comes from various natural forces that increase the death rate. This may easily happen to us, but so far, except for war-making, we have used our intellectual skill almost exclusively to *lower* the death rate by minimizing the effects of the natural controls. Since the living tend to vote against death while the unborn have little political clout, this trend seems likely to continue; we must therefore devote our attention to control of the birth rate. Such social factors as urbanization and industrialization have tended to lower birth rates in the developed countries, but many experts question whether the ultimately necessary goal of zero population growth can be attained without additional, externally applied measures. At the moment, however, the main difficulty is in the underdeveloped countries, where poverty, social traditions, lack of communication, and technical inadequacies have tended to contribute to birth rates that are increasingly out of balance with rapidly dropping death rates and that pose ever increasing social and economic problems. A zero population growth rate in the developed countries, even if attainable at present, would not only have little effect on the world total, but would threaten a disastrous shortage of trained humans at just the time when technical skills will be most needed.

The second problem, which is compounded by the first, involves our exploitation of the environment. Demands for food are, of course, tied to the population but the high animal protein diet of the developed countries makes very heavy extra demands on space, plant food, and water for these secondary food sources. We are not now feeding the world, and it is questionable whether food resources, even for the short term, can catch up to the population at present growth rates. Water demands are closely tied to those for agricultural products, but industrialization and urbanization bring enormously increased per capita use of metered water. In the United States we seem near the limit of water resoures now. With many metals and some non-metals we see again in the developed countries huge increases in individual use, with the accelerating exponential of human population again compounding the rate of increase. Per capita energy requirements, in particular, have mounted astronomically in the United States with no end in sight. The 6 percent of the world's population that is in this country now uses about 50 percent of the world's resources, yet there is little doubt that the rest of the world desires most strongly to achieve an equivalent material standard of living. One needs only to reflect on the fact that mainland China has four times our population but that we use about 150 times as much electrical power per person. Also where we have one motor vehicle per two inhabitants, the half-billion people of India have about one per seven hundred, the nearly one billion mainland Chinese perhaps one per two to three thousand.

It seems to be implicit in our thinking to bring the rest of the world up to acceptable standards of living. We have hindered attainment of this goal by our steady inflation of the definition of "acceptable." But simultaneously those most actively concerned with the population question and with resources appear mostly to think in terms of how many people the world can accommodate at whatever miserable level—as though we were engaged in some sort of wretched endurance contest instead of an effort to improve man's lot. It is altogether too likely that we shall substitute endless compromises and inch-by-inch downgrading of our standard of living for the long-term planning that our future problems obviously require. We can no longer afford parochial or nationalistic thinking. We cannot, for example, afford much longer the luxury of ignoring one-fourth of the human race because we are not on speaking terms. That the attempt to understand each other occupies more and more of our time and attention becomes comprehensible when one realizes that the number of links of communication among members of a group is itself an exponential function of a number that is already not only an exponential but an accelerating exponential.

In discussing the population explosion I find a curious dichotomy—adults seldom do little more than view with alarm and assume that someone will cope; college students want to know what can be done—but done instantly. I am afraid that the related problems are going to be an increasing concern of the entire race for generations and that our main effort should be to impress the facts on as many people as possible now and to raise the next generation to consider overpopulation and overconsumption as our number one responsibilities. I do not want to deprecate one-day campaigns of litter collection and the boycotting of phosphate detergents by militant housewives. They serve to dramatize the issue. But I do want to stress that we must not dismiss the world's population dilemma and our responsibility to it by immediate and individual contributions. We are confronted with a crisis of the entire race that will extend into the indefinite future until we bring our numbers into balance with our resources and environment. Intellectuals must take the long-term view and help primarily by using their undoubted abilities for communication, persuasion, education, and influence. The donning of hair shirts will have little effect beyond convincing the rest of the world once more that intellectuals are a bunch of nuts—a work of supererogation.

As to the rest of us in the United States, I am afraid that our most direct, if grim and uninspired, contribution will be in the form of taxes. It is we who have largely established the present opulent living standards, it is we who have been largely responsible for exploiting and polluting the world. Now the bill must be paid, and it is only fair that we in the United States must pay a large part of it. People must be educated, research must de done, techniques must be developed in all of the problem areas that we have considered. The results must not only be used to alleviate our predicaments but must be made available throughout the world. In only a few countries are the trained people and facilities available; there can be little doubt that we must take the lead.

Obviously the underdeveloped countries must, in the long

run, train and use their own technical cadres to manage their own difficulties, but the training must come initially from the developed countries. Unfortunately students sent to the United States have shown a distressing tendency, when competent, to stay. The alternative of sending American educators abroad has not proved very successful, yet this cycle must be broken.

Throughout this discussion we have seen scientific and technical questions of immense importance. In many instances we shall be confronted with alternatives among which we simply cannot make rational choices for lack of basic facts. But these are times in which support for basic scientific research is waning, in which anti-intellectual feeling is achieving new heights, and in which the scientist is being blamed for everything from the war to pollution. Among the myriad problems that confront us with inadequate answers one might cite the question of how (or if) fusion power is to be made available. It is difficult to think of a development that could be of greater importance, yet nuclear physics is suffering painfully from lack of expansion or even continuance of present fundamental work. In the most important area of birth control we have lagged miserably because of lack of basic knowledge of the biology of human reproduction. The informed public is now demanding instant answers to questions in social and ecological science, where the ground work is largely missing. In addition we need an explosion of application of *existing* knowledge. A large proportion of the technically trained must turn to applied science even if it means eschewing the theoretical side of science, which has always been so much more alluring to the talented. But at the same time we must not be dragooned into abandoning fundamental science because, as all scientists know, that is the goose that lays the golden egg for the future. It will take a committee of Solomons to achieve a balance, a Newtonian Demonsthenes to talk Congress into supporting the effort, taxpayers with the patience of Job and the altruism of

Pollyanna, science with the selfless dedication of old Rover. I don't know that we have it in us.

A colleague in the business school quizzed me industriously for an hour about the population crisis and then told me that I was never going to accomplish anything by frightening people. What is needed, he said, is to show business men opportunities to make money out of our difficulties. Then solutions will come. I am sure he is right. I wish that I had sent him a consultation bill for $500 to impress on him the seriousness of the situation. It is already obvious that a number of firms have understood that there is money to be made in curing pollution even with our present technology. It can scarcely be doubted that research on innumerable ramifications of questions already raised in this and other similar books can scarcely fail to find demand beyond the dreams of avarice. Barring catastrophe, the pressures that we feel on every hand in the United States today will be world-wide in the very near future.

But can business adjust to the idea of an economy that does not demand an annual rate of 2 percent expansion of the population to thrive? Can we adjust to living within our means? Is the question how to raise the world to our material standard of living? Or is it whether we can afford to do so? And if we decide that we cannot exploit the environment to support our present population, far less the projected hordes of the future, what shall we do? Control the numbers of the putative hordes? Lower our standards? Pull everyone toward a level of common survival rather than adjust the human population to its environment? Or are we in the United States going to try to retreat to an armed insularity while the rest of the world squabbles in adject poverty? It seems significant that both the U.S.S.R. and China put ICBM's ahead of consumer goods.

While we consider these questions, every hour we are adding about 8000 people to the human race. This is not just births, but births minus deaths. We are adding to the world population each two days a city nearly the size of Indianapolis, each year nearly the population of Japan. The growth of human population *will* be regulated either naturally and possibly catastrophically or through our own intelligent action. Unlike any other creature the human has the ability to solve his population problem. The only question is whether he will—in time.

Suggested Readings

The following offer more detailed information on the topics covered in this book. A number of them have been referred to in the text.

GENERAL

Ehrlich, Paul. *The Population Bomb*. New York: Ballantine Books, 1968. A popular, dramatic discussion of the population problem.

Ehrlich, Paul and Anne H. Ehrlich. *Population, Resources, and Environment*. San Francisco: W. H. Freeman Co., 1970. A thorough, detailed textbook and source of data.

EMPHASIS ON POPULATION AND ITS CONTROL

Ng, L.K.Y., and Stuart Mudd, editors. *The Population Crisis*. Bloomington: Indiana University Press, 1966. A collection of articles by recognized authorities.

American Friends Service Committee. *Who Shall Live*. New York: Hill and Wang, 1970. Birth control, abortion, planned parenthood.

Appleman, Philip. *The Silent Explosion*. Boston: Beacon Press, 1965. A detailed review of the Catholic position on birth control.

EMPHASIS ON RESOURCES OF FOOD, WATER, MINERALS, ETC.

Brown, Harrison; James Bonner; and John Weir. *The Next Hundred Years*. New York: The Viking Press, 1963. A pioneer source book.

Committee on Resources and Man of the National Research Council and the National Academy of Sciences (U.S.). *Resources and Man*. San Francisco: W. H. Freeman Co., 1969.

Paddock, William and Paul Paddock. *Famine 1975*. Boston: Little, Brown, 1967. Hopefully an overdrawn but nonetheless chilling projection of our immediate food needs and resources world-wide.

Brown, Lester R. *Seeds of Change*. New York: Praeger Publishers, 1970. The potentialities of the "green revolution."

Wright, Jim. *The Coming Water Famine*. New York: Coward-McCann, 1966. A grim but convincing discussion of the approaching water crisis in the United States.

Suggested Readings

Emphasis on Ecology—*(the interrelationship of man and his environment)*

Scientific American (entire issue). *The Biosphere.* September, 1970.

Dasmann, Raymond F. *Environmental Conservation.* New York: John Wiley and Sons, 1959. A new edition of a classic text.

Cox, George W. *Readings in Conservation Ecology.* New York: Appleton-Century-Crofts, 1969.

Pollution

Wright, Jim (see above). The sad picture of water pollution in the United States.

National Tuberculosis and Respiratory Disease Association. *Air Pollution Primer.*

To keep up with current ideas and developments, one can follow a number of periodicals intended (in order) for audiences from the general reader to the scientifically trained. All have shown steady concern for the population problem and its ramifications.

Science News (Science Service, Washington, D.C.)

The Sciences (The New York Academy of Sciences)

Scientific American

Bioscience (The American Institute of Biological Sciences)

American Scientist (The Society of Sigma Xi)

Science (The American Association for the Advancement of Sciences)

Index

Africa: population control, 20, 43, 45, 60, 196, 210, 213, 230; modernization, 133, 181, 182, 230–31

Agency for International Development (AID), 200–01

Agriculture: land use for, 32, 33, 47, 48, 50, 51, 58, 182, 207; efficiency, 41, 46, 47, 56, 71–72, 122, 156–57; vs. aquaculture, 56; experts, 59; and water loss, 89–90, 95; and birth rate, 202–04

Agronomy, 58

Air, 11, 124

Air conditioning, 83, 85

Air pollution. See Pollution

Airports: land use for, 35

Alfalfa: as food, 65, 66, 74, 83

Algae: as food, 52, 67, 68, 116; and eutrophication, 69, 142–45, 147, 148, 149, 171

Aluminum: resources, 106–08

Amino acids: synthetic, need, 70

Antartic. See Polar regions

Antibiotics, 70

Aquaculture, 55–57

Aquifers, 93

Arctic. See Polar regions

Asia, 43, 47, 58, 133, 230–31

Astronauts: water use by, 96–97

Atmosphere, 102, 131, 132–34, 191

Atomic bomb, 109

Atomic Energy Commission, 166

Atomic fall-out, 163

Atomic power. See Power, nuclear

Audubon Society, 35, 181

Automobile: deaths from, 15, 127, 156, 186, 205; and American mores, 57, 204, 207, 228; vs. environment, 89, 111, 116–17, 118, 122, 126, 129–30, 132–33, 154, 169, 172, 178, 235

Bacteria: model population, 9–11, 22, 23; size, 10; factors limiting, 11, 119–20; convert wastes, 51, 52; as food, 69–70; balance ecology, 171; endanger man, 183

Barrows, John E., 56

Bays. See Coastal waters

Birds: and conservationists, 69, 181; in polluted waters, 145; and petroleum leakage, 153; and pesticides, 158, 159–60, 162; and insect population, 180

Birth control: and population, 21–22, 194, 232; in U.S., 194, 195, 201; national policies of, 195, 213, 218, 219, 221; and Pope, 197; methods of, 197–98, 200, 211–12, 213, 215–19, 220, 224, 226, 227; and political attitudes, 200–01; obstacles to, 200, 202, 203–05, 210, 223; ethics and morals, 202, 226–29; and motivation, 204, 210, 211, 212, 214, 222, 224; in underdeveloped areas, 211–14, 216; research, 220, 232, 237

Birth rate: in various areas, 20, 198, 215, 229–30; and population, 21, 27; causes and effects of, 24, 194, 202, 203, 205, 230–31, 234; and national policy, 194, 195, 213, 218, 219, 221, 231

Blake, Judith, 195

Bower, C. A., 49

Bradley, Charles C., 82–84, 88–91

Brown, Lester, R., 76

Burbank, Luther, 62, 95

Business: and expansionism, 204–05

Cancer: and hormonal pill, 216

Carbohydrate, 66

Carbon dioxide, 72, 73, 80, 111, 131, 169

Carbon fuel. See Fossil fuel

Carson, Rachel, 61, 155

Catholic church: and birth rate, 3, 20, 198, 232; and birth control, 194–201, 218, 223

Index

Cattle. *See* Food
Chemicals: from fossil fuel, 114
Children: malnutrition in, 42; number wanted, 195–96, 214; motives for having, 203, 213; and divorce, 226; illegitimate, 228
China. *See* Communist China; Taiwan
Chromite: demand and cost, 107
Climate. *See* Weather
Coal: as a raw material, 71, 117; fossil fuel, 109, 113, 114, 134; and pollution, 132–34
Coale, Ansley, 15
Coastal waters: pollution of, 148, 150–51, 152–55, 158, 177; and land-fill, 170–71
Coliform count, 137, 140–41
Communication, 208–13, 230, 232, 235
Communist China: and population, 3, 105, 181–82, 194, 204; food problems, 43, 45; material demands, 105, 133, 234, 235, 238; and pollution, 138, 165; and nuclear war, 165, 185, 194, 238
Compartmentalization, 205–07
Competitors: and population control, 11, 24, 26–27, 180, 187, 191
Composting: municipal, 172
Compound exponential. *See* Growth rate
Conservation, 34–35, 69, 94–95, 147
Consumer goods: vs. resources, 118
Copper, 80, 104, 106, 118
Corn, 41, 45, 63, 64, 71–72
Cotton, 33, 84, 158
Curtis, Richard B., 208

Dairy production, 41
Davis, Kingsley, 205, 222–24, 229
DDT. *See* Pesticides
Deafness: from noise, 174, 175
Death: causes, 19–21, 127, 156
Death rate, 15, 17–21, 27, 233
Demography. *See* Population
Desalination, 98–100
Desert: use of, 36, 48, 49, 79
Desmond, Annabelle, 14
Detergents, 145, 153, 236
Developed countries, 20, 111, 192, 236–37
Diet. *See* Food

Disease: and population control, 14, 24, 25, 183–84, 186, 187, 192; control of, by pesticides, 61, 156; from pollution 128, 137, 145, 151, 163–65, 175–76; noise, 175; and war, 183–84, 186; and natural disaster, 183–84; and birth control, 215–17
Divorce, 226
Donora, Pennsylvania, 126–27, 129
Doom-saying, 21, 77, 117–18, 147
Dorf, Erling, 131–32
Du Bridge, Lee, 124
Dumps, 131, 169, 170
Dust bowl, 52, 102

Earth: atmosphere change, 131–35
Ecology: of population, 4, 23, 231, 234–38; and fish crop, 52–54; and pollution, 99–100, 151, 152–55, 166–68, 170–71; and pesticides, 160–62; exploitation of, 236
Economics: and population problem, 49–51, 172–73, 234; pressure for birth control, 224; and ZPG, 238
Edmondson, W. T., 147–48
Education, 195, 205–06, 230, 232
Eisenhower, Pres. Dwight D., 199–200
Emigration: to other planets, 38, 39
Endrin, 157–58
Energy: and weather, 101–02, 123–25; demands of man, 111, 134, 192
Environment. *See* Ecology
Epidemics. *See* Disease
Escherichia coli. See Coliform count
Estuaries. *See* Coastal waters
Europe: birth rate, 20, 198, 214, 219, 230; fertilizer use, 60; and pollution, 102, 133, 149, 173; automobiles, 133; Catholic influence in, 198
Euthanasia in U.S., 19
Eutrophication, 142–48, 166
Ewell, Raymond, 43, 44, 59, 60
Expansionism: 203–04
Extinction: and evolution, 23, 26; human, 27, 185–87; animal, 159–60, 181–82

Family planning: effectiveness, 21, 222, 223; as national policy, 21, 22, 194, 201, 221–22; obstacles to, 201, 202, 212

Famine, 25, 77, 186, 231
Fecundity: human drive toward, 195–96, 203, 214
Fertilizer, 58–60, 64–65, 73, 74, 145, 172
Fish: potential crop, 52–55, 155; overfishing, 53–54, 151; aquaculture, shellfish, 55–57; pollution, 138, 142–45, 154, 155, 158
Fish Protein Concentrate (FPC), 40, 54–55
Fission. *See* Power, nuclear
Flood control, 32, 94, 98
Food: and population, 4, 11, 22, 24, 74, 88, 191, 206, 207, 234; animals as source of, 35, 56, 57, 65–66, 68, 83–84, 139; surplus, 41, 44, 45, 46; dietary standards, 43, 45–46, 82–83, 91; losses, 46, 84, 183, 207; increasing production, 47, 55–56, 61, 63, 75–77, 100, 155, 157, 168; new sources, 48–52, 55, 57, 65–71, 114, 116; diminishing supplies, 53, 54, 150–51, 155; cost, 55, 65–66, 67, 68; chains, 66, 69, 158, 159, 164; plants as sources of, 73–74, 89
Ford foundation, 63
Forests: space, 32–33, 36; conservation, 34; food production, 35, 51–52, 70; water consumption, 85
Fossil fuel: power source, 109, 111, 113–14, 117, 191; consumption of, 114, 134–35, 191; and nuclear power, 117
Fusion. *See* Power, nuclear

Garbage disposal, 172–73
Gas: natural, 109, 113
Genetics: human, 19–21, 163, 165; plant, 41, 59–60, 62–64, 73, 74; animal, 63, 162
Ghettoes, 45, 184
Glaciation. *See* Ice age
Gold, 81, 106–07
Grassland, 34–45, 52, 66
Great Lakes, 92–93, 142–46, 152, 177
Greenberg, D. S., 199
Greenhouse effect, 131
"Green revolution," 64
Growth rate: exponential, 3, 4, 6–11, 14, 27, 40, 74–75, 191, 205–06, 233;

compounded, 14, 118, 171–72, 192, 233, 234; levels-off, 22

Health: and population, 21, 25
Heat balance, 131–35
Heating: domestic, 116–17, 129
Heredity. *See* Genetics
Hickman, Kenneth, 134
Highways, 35, 36
Hitler, Adolph, 194
Housing, 32, 207

Ice age: and carbon dioxide, 132
Illegitimacy, 227–28
Immorality: and love marriage, 228
Immortality, 15–22
Incinerators, 169, 170
India: population, 3, 64, 105, 133, 156, 195, 206, 212, 222, 230, 235; and starvation, 42–46, 59, 60, 64, 183, 210; governmental inadequacy, 46, 59, 138, 210, 230; agriculture, 59, 60, 64, 183; material demands, 105, 133, 235; birth control, 195, 212, 218, 222
Indifference. *See* Compartmentalization
Industrialization: and birth rate, 20, 21, 223, 234; and material demands, 80, 86–87, 105, 108, 118, 192, 234
Industry: need for, 32, 59, 60, 62, 155–56, 238; demands on resources, 52–54, 86, 94, 98–99; and pollution, 120, 122, 126–27, 129, 130, 132, 139–41, 150, 154–56, 166–67, 176–79
Information explosion, 208
Insecticides. *See* Pesticides
Insects: vs. man, 46, 59, 180, 183
Involvement. *See* Compartmentalization
Iron, 81, 107–08, 109
Irrigation, 35, 49, 89, 94, 98–99, 102, 168
Isaac Walton League, 35

Japan: birth control, 21, 210, 214, 219, 221, 223, 230; food in, 48, 53, 56, 60, 67, 73; fishing, aquaculture, 53, 56, 69; pollution, 153, 173
Joos, Lother A., 102
Jukes, Thomas H., 156

Kennedy, Pres. John F., 200

Index

Lakes: water resources, 92, 98, 141; Erie, 92–93, 138, 142–46; Huron, 92–93; Michigan, 93, 146, 159; Superior, 93, 146; Tahoe, 147–48, 177; Washington, 147–48, 150, 177; Mendota, 148–49; Cayuga, 165–67
Land use, 22, 31–38, 47, 48, 50, 51, 58, 89, 94, 98, 150, 207
Land-fill, 131, 169, 170–71
Latin America, 20, 198, 201–02, 230
Lead, 106, 129
Legislation: birth right, 234
Liability: for pollution, 154
Life: average length, 16–20; expectancy, 3, 16–18, 156; span, 17–21
Limnology, 147–49
Living standards, 235
Lumber, 85

McMillan, J.R.A., 85
Mao Tse-tung, 194
Malnutrition, 42–43, 55, 77, 193
Malthus, Thomas Robert, 5, 6, 71–72, 75–76, 104, 106, 107
Manganese: demand and cost, 107
Marine biology, 54
Marriage, 226–28
Mead, Margaret, 226–27, 229
Medicine, 3, 20, 21
Metals. See Minerals
Metcalf, Ralph L., 157
Mexico, 19–20, 63, 64, 65
Miller, Albert, 171
Minerals: resources, 104, 106–07, 108, 193, 207, 234; demand for, 105–06, 108, 111; energy-producing, 108
Molybdenum: demand and cost, 107
Morality: and birth control, 226–29
Mortality. See Death rate
Muller, Herman J., 163
Mussolini, Benito, 194

National Institutes of Health, 199
Nationalism: and population, 194, 196, 221–24, 235
Neiberger, M., 123
Nickel: demand and cost, 107
Nitrate, 145, 148
Noise: effects on people, 174–75

Ocean: food from, 40, 52–55, 68, 74–75; as water source, 79, 81, 98; as cesspool, 141, 150, 158

Oil. See Fossil fuel; Petroleum
Old age: death from, 19–21
Ore. See Minerals
ORSANCO, 137, 177
Over-fishing. See fish

Pakistan, 43, 63, 64, 65, 222
Paper consumption, 85, 169
Paper mills. See Industry; Pollution
Parks: land use for, 33, 34, 89
Paving: and land use, 32, 33, 35, 36, 89, 94
Permafrost: and water problems, 79
Pesticides: and crop yields, 58, 60–62, 73, 114, 155, 157, 161; and human health, 61, 156, 158, 161, 162; pollution by, 141, 151, 155–62, 168; animals killed by, 151, 157–62; and ecology, 158–60, 161–62, 168
Petroleum: as food source, 71; exhaustible resource, 71, 80, 113; energy from, 108–13; pollution from, 132–33, 134, 152–54
Phosphate, 108, 145, 148
Photosynthesis: food source, 66, 68, 72–74; energy source, 80, 109
Plankton, 153, 158
Planned Parenthood, 203, 212–13, 218–19, 226–29
Plants. See Food, Photosynthesis
Plass, Gilbert N., 131–32
Plastics: from fossil fuels, 114
Plutonium: and nuclear power, 109
Polar regions, 36, 79, 81, 102, 158
Politics: and politicians, 46, 185
Pollution: solutions, 122, 123–26, 129–30, 133, 134, 136, 137, 141, 145–46, 148–50, 168, 171, 173, 177–79, 236, 238
—contributions by: individuals, 4, 25, 114, 122, 129, 135, 137, 139–41, 145–47, 152, 154, 169–74, 172, 205, 207; industry, 114, 115–17, 122, 126, 129, 130, 139, 140, 141, 146, 152–54, 163, 165–67, 176–77; automobile, 122, 129, 178, 205, 207
—costs of: to individual, 129, 170, 176–78, 179, 236; to recreation and tourism, 137, 140, 141, 142, 147, 148–49, 150, 152, 153–54, 155, 167, 171; to industry, 154, 164, 167, 176–77, 179

—damage to: animals as food sources, 53, 56, 122, 140, 144–45, 150–51, 153–54, 158, 166; water supply, 56, 92, 96, 135–37, 139, 140–44, 150, 177–78; weather, 102; buildings, cities, 119, 127–28, 129; human health, 119, 121, 122, 126, 127, 128, 137–38, 142, 151, 158, 161, 162, 163, 165, 174–76, 179, 193; coastal waters, 150–51, 152–55

Pope Paul VI, 197, 201, 205.

Population: growth rate, 3, 15, 21, 23, 64, 74–75, 76, 80, 101, 132, 150, 171, 187, 191, 202, 221–22, 233, 234, 235–36, 238–39; limit of and ZPG, 11, 22, 23, 24–25, 74–75, 191, 192, 194, 205, 231, 233, 234, 236, 238; regulation, 11, 21, 22, 23, 24, 27, 180, 186, 192 205, 221–26, 232, 233–34, 239; doubling time, 12–16, 27, 233; size (demography), 13–14, 22, 23, 24, 37, 74–75, 88, 165, 179, 180, 183–84, 186, 193, 198–99, 202, 208–11, 233, 235–36, 239; and standard of living, 37, 38, 39, 76, 103, 192–93, 235; nationalism and under-population, 194, 196, 210, 231, 235, 238

Poverty, 45, 91, 180, 184, 195, 202, 212, 213

Power: electrical, 35, 36, 78, 91, 98, 109, 111, 115, 117, 133, 164, 167, 235

Power, nuclear: nuclear fission, 99–100, 114–15, 117, 133, 152, 164, 166–67; as energy source, 108, 114–17, 134; nuclear fusion, 109–10, 114–15, 117, 133, 134, 152, 165, 167, 173, 237; and pollution, 152, 163–65, 166, 210

Predators. *See* Competitors

Pressure: social, 195, 202, 223, 224, 228, 234

Protein: animal, 65, 66, 68, 234; plant, 66, 67, 68, 71; cost of, 66, 67, 68

Public health, 183–84

Radiation: heat from earth, 131; and nuclear power, 162, 163, 164, 210

Railroads: land use for, 36

Rainfall, 50, 81, 88, 94, 100

Rat: vs. man, 24, 46, 59, 183

Recreation, 32, 89, 98, 150

Recycling resources, 172, 173, 178

Resources: exhaustion of, 6; demand for, 42–43, 80, 81, 83–84, 86, 106, 108, 110–11, 118, 134, 171–72, 208, 233–35; technological, 230–31

Rice: "Miracle," 46, 59–60, 63, 64, 71–72, 73, 76

Rockefeller Foundation, 63

Rosen, Samuel, 175

Roueché, Berton, 126–27

Rubbish, 124

Ryther, John H., 56

Salinity, 49

Schmitt, Walter R., 52, 75

Science, 5, 206–07, 210, 237

Septic systems, 147, 154

Sewage, 56, 70, 71, 94, 136–41, 145, 148, 172, 177

Shellfish, 53, 54–57, 150, 151, 154, 159

Sierra Club, 35

Silent Spring, 60, 61, 155, 159–60

Silver, 106–07

Slums, 45, 184

Smog, 121–22

Social structure, 26, 184, 185, 203

Social science, 234, 237

Social work, 212–13

Solar energy, 73, 108, 109, 111, 114, 125, 134

Space: living, 22, 37

SST: and noise, 175

Starvation, 43, 45, 77

Steel, 106–07

Stenert, William, 175

Stycos, J. M., 198

Sukarno, Pres., of Indonesia, 194

Sulfur, 108, 140

Sweden: and birth control, 196

Taiwan, 196, 217, 221–23

Taxes, 34, 98, 177, 204–05, 224, 236

Technology, 230, 234

Temperature inversion. *See* Pollution

Thermal pollution. *See* Pollution

Thorium: and nuclear power, 109

Tin: demand and cost, 107

Tobacco: per capita use, 83, 84

Tourism: cost of, 32, 142, 147, 150

Transportation, 32, 35

Trash: use of, 51, 52, 71, 80, 172, 173; disposal of, 115, 122, 131, 168–74, 178, 236

Index

Tropics: and agriculture, 48, 50
Tundra: and land use, 36, 79

Underdeveloped countries: needs, 57, 58, 59–60, 61, 62, 105, 113, 200, 235; population problems, 211–12, 213–14, 229–30, 234
"Underpopulated" countries, 194, 196, 210
United Nations, 198–99, 201, 203
United States: population and growth, 33, 75, 207, 215, 230, 231, 236; land use in, 47–48, 50; minerals and energy, resources and demands, 60, 129, 130, 133, 164, 234, 235; food production and demands, 83–84, 210; pollution, 94, 102; water resources and demands, 142, 234
Universities, 148–49, 227–28
Uranium, 109, 114
Urbanization: and lower birth rate, 20, 21, 202–03, 212, 223, 230, 234; and demands on resources, 80, 86–87, 105, 118, 192, 234; and pollution, 128, 175, 179
U.S.S.R., 20, 42, 230, 238

Van Helmont, Jan Baptista, 72
Victorianism: and birth control, 194
Viruses. *See* Disease
Vitamins: synthetic, 70

War, nuclear: and population, 5, 24, 184–86, 187, 194, 233, 238; and pollution, 162–65
Waste: human. *See* Sewage
—solid. *See* Trash
Water: problems, 32, 49, 88, 89, 92–95, 98–100, 103, 111, 136–37, 145, 205, 206–07; use, 73, 74, 81–86, 88, 89–91, 92–94, 137, 167, 234; resources, 78–79, 81, 88–94, 98, 115–16, 141, 142; recycling, 80, 95–97, 136–37, 150; in the future, 86–87, 89, 90–91, 93, 94, 100–01, 115, 116, 207; loss, 89–90; cost, 98–99, 103, 116, 137, 150
Watershed areas. *See* Conservation
Weather modification, 101–02
Welfare: and birth control, 195, 213
Wheat: surplus, 44, 45–46, 59; growing of, 62, 63, 64, 66, 68, 73, 76, 82, 157; as food, 67, 68
World Health Organization. *See* U.N.
Women: and birth control, 20, 195, 205, 211, 220, 224
Woodwell, George M., 158
Wool: per capita use of, 83, 84

Yeast: as food, 69–70

Zero population growth (ZPG), 22, 195–96, 205, 231, 234
Zinc: demand for, 106